MUMPS, MEASLES & MOSAICS

A NEW NATURALIST SPECIAL VOLUME

The aim of THE NEW NATURALIST series is to interest the general reader in the wild life of Britain by recapturing the inquiring spirit of the old naturalists. The Editors believe that the natural pride of the British public in their native fauna and flora, to which must be added concern for their conservation, is best fostered by maintaining a high standard of accuracy combined with clarity of exposition in presenting the results of modern scientific research. The volumes in the main series deal with large groups of animals and plants, with the natural history of particular areas or habitats in Britain, and with certain special subjects. THE NEW NATURALIST SPECIAL VOLUMES, on the other hand, cover, in greater detail, a single species or group of species. In both the main series and specials the animals and plants are described in relation to their homes and habitats, and are portrayed in their full beauty with the help of both colour and monochrome photographs.

EDITORS:
JAMES FISHER M.A.
JOHN GILMOUR M.A.
JULIAN HUXLEY M.A. D.Sc. F.R.S.
L. DUDLEY STAMP C.B.E. D.Lit. D.Sc.

PHOTOGRAPHIC EDITOR:
ERIC HOSKING F.R.P.S.

Caption on page XII

MUMPS, MEASLES & MOSAICS

A STUDY OF ANIMAL AND PLANT VIRUSES

by

KENNETH M. SMITH
D.FC. F.R.S
HONORARY FELLOW
DOWNING COLLEGE, CAMBRIDGE

and

ROY MARKHAM
M.A. PH.D.

*Illustrated with 25 Photographs
and 10 Diagrams*

FREDERICK A. PRAEGER
NEW YORK

BOOKS THAT MATTER

Published in the United States of America in 1954
by Frederick A. Praeger, Inc., Publishers,
105 West 40th Street, New York, 18, N.Y.

Library of Congress Catalog Card Number: 54-9295

Printed in Great Britain

CONTENTS

LIST OF PLATES

EDITORS' PREFACE

WE MAKE NO APOLOGY for including a volume on viruses in the *New Naturalist* series, although it is a subject which does not, perhaps, immediately suggest itself in connection with British Natural History in the traditional sense. Not only are viruses of outstanding scientific interest among living things (if they can, indeed, be classed as living!), but, by the diseases they cause, they exert a profound effect on many of the animals and plants of our countryside.

The authors of the present volume have included all aspects of the subject in their survey, but they have dealt in greatest detail with viruses associated with plants and insects, rather than with the higher animals and man, since their own work has lain principally in this field. Dr. Kenneth Smith, in co-operation with Dr. Roy Markham and other workers, has built up at Cambridge a school of investigation of world-wide reputation and has shown in this and other books that he knows how to explain the results of his researches—and those of others—in clear and arresting language.

Viruses, as we have implied, have two quite distinct, though interrelated, claims on our interest—one mainly scientific, the other mainly practical. The latter is the more obvious. The mere names of such diseases as smallpox, foot-and-mouth, influenza and the common cold are enough to show the vital importance of viruses to man, and there are several equally serious plant diseases—the " mosaics " of the title, for example— whose names are less well known to the public. The story of the discovery of the cause of these diseases, their method of trans- mission and, in unfortunately too few cases, their control, is a fascinating one. Many people are familiar with the part played by insects, especially greenfly, in the transmission of virus diseases, but the viruses that actually attack insects, as opposed to being passively carried and transmitted by them, are not so well known. The authors deal fully with these and with the experiments now being carried out to control insect pests, including clothes moths, by infecting them with the appropriate lethal virus. The reverse process, the control of the viruses causing disease, has proved extremely difficult. Too often, as in foot-and-mouth disease, the only method for preventing spread seems to be destruction of the victims; in other cases, like the common cold (where destruction is hardly a practical policy!), we are forced to let the infection run its course. Sometimes, however, something can be done, and in the present volume, the authors give much practical advice to gardeners and others on the identification of virus diseases and on the control of those that can be controlled.

On the more purely scientific aspect of their subject, the authors give a fascinating account of the gradual discovery of the nature of viruses—their unbelievably small size, their unique methods of propagation, and, above all, their borderland status between life and not-life. Some of them at least can be crystallised out in the form of pure chemical substances; yet they are alive in the sense that they are self-reproducing, though none have been found capable of leading an independent existence. Whatever proves to be the truth about their origin, they must in any case be similar in many ways to the primitive forms first adopted by living matter on this planet. In recent years the electron microscope, magnifying many thousands of times, has enabled scientists to study the shapes and behaviour of the actual virus bodies, and a number of striking photographs, taken with the aid of this new tool of science, are included in this book.

The advances in our knowledge of viruses during the last thirty years have been spectacular; thirty years hence many of the present mysteries concerning them may have been solved by the army of workers all over the world now attacking the problem. In the meantime, we are glad that we have persuaded two distinguished leaders to set down, for the general public, an up-to-date account of the present state of the battle.

THE EDITORS

AUTHORS' PREFACE

As THE EDITORS have pointed out, no apology is necessary for writing a book about viruses. These agents play such a large part in the life of every one of us that the time has now come for the intelligent reader to know something of what is meant by the term " Virus Disease." All through his life from the time of vaccination, usually before his first birthday, man has viruses forced upon his notice. So far as his own health is concerned, he must run the gauntlet of mumps, measles, influenza, polio-myelitis, herpes, shingles, the common cold and so on. Anyone in England who wants to grow potatoes must obtain his " seed " potatoes from special areas in Scotland or Northern Ireland because " seed " saved from English-grown potatoes are full of virus. The owner of the pedigree herd of cattle is never sure when his beasts may have to be slaughtered and burned because of the virus of foot-and-mouth disease. The poultry farmer now faces a similar threat because of the prevalence of the virus of fowl pest, and even the silk industry must keep an ever watchful eye on the silkworms for the first signs of the virus disease known as " jaundice." Only recently a new threat has arisen, and the production of the antibiotics, penicillin and streptomycin, is menaced by viruses which destroy the fungi themselves.

Apart from this gloomy side of the picture, there is the scientific study of the viruses which, shorn of its technicalities, is one of the greatest fascination. So many of the problems border upon the study of life itself. What of the latent viruses found by chance in what appear to be perfectly healthy organisms? What are they doing there and how did they get there? Or are they a normal part of this particular organism and only become a virus when they are transferred to another type of host ? Have latent viruses anything to do with cancer? We know that some

tumours are caused by viruses. Where did the " swollen-shoot "
virus come from which is destroying the cocoa industry of the
Gold Coast? Was this a virus latent in some quite different
plant which was brought by chance to the cocoa trees? What do
viruses look like? The electron microscope has answered that
question and we know now the shape and appearance of many
different types of viruses. Some at least of these questions are
discussed in this book and we hope that the reader, though he
will not find out what a virus is, may perhaps find an interesting
account of what a virus can do.

Many of the illustrations in this book are original. Those
which have been kindly lent are acknowledged in each case to
the author concerned. Our thanks are due to Miss Margaret
Short for making the drawings illustrating Figs. 4-7 (pp. 133-36).

K. M. S.
R. M.

Caption to Frontispiece

1, Head of cock infected with fowl pox. 2, Turnip yellow mosaic: the virus
is transmitted by a flea-beetle. 3, Wallflower infected with the cabbage black
ringspot virus: note the flower " break " in the form of yellow flecks. 4,
Tulips showing the colour " break " induced by an aphid-transmitted virus.

CHAPTER I

INTRODUCTORY

To UNDERSTAND the viruses, the subject of this book, we must look back a little over the past history of the science we now call microbiology, and review some of the events which have made this study possible. We know that bacteria existed long before man; for example, Haggard states that signs of infection can be found in the fossil teeth of dinosaurs, cave bears, and sabretoothed tigers. Moreover, in one skeleton of a horned dinosaur, marks of an abscess in the leg were seen which must once have held about half a gallon of pus.

But right up to the seventeenth century, man was in complete ignorance of the existence of the infinitely small world of microbiology. The door to this new world was opened by a Dutch draper, Antony van Leeuwenhoek, who was born in Delft in 1632. About this time the age of superstition was gradually giving place to an epoch when men were no longer willing to accept any fable merely because their fathers before them had believed it, and one of the first of these sceptics was van Leeuwenhoek. He had a great interest in making magnifying lenses, and this interest developed into a passion which led him to devote the greater part of his life to perfecting his microscopes. His curiosity was insatiable and he examined every conceivable object which could be placed under his lenses.

Leeuwenhoek was certainly an original thinker, and one of his ideas, fantastic to the modern chemist, played an important part in his subsequent observations. He wanted to know why pepper was hot to the taste, and believing that the peppercorns contained large numbers of tiny sharp particles which pricked the tongue, he tried to examine them with his microscope but found them, not unnaturally, somewhat difficult to manipulate. Thinking to soften them and render them more adaptable to his needs, he placed them in a basin of water and left them for some days. When he came to examine the peppercorns again, he observed in the water large numbers of what he called " little animals." These were undoubtedly bacteria and van Leeuwenhoek was the first man to see them.

In his untiring quest for more material for his microscope, van Leeuwenhoek collected some rain-water from the gutters of his house and examined a drop under his lenses. He was astonished to find, even in the rain-water, more " little animals." " Can it be," he wondered, " that these little animals fall from heaven? " But van Leeuwenhoek was one who took nothing for granted and tested all his theories with a thoroughness which might be copied with advantage by some present-day scientists. He obtained a shallow dish, washed it thoroughly, and then placed it in his garden to catch some rain-water falling directly into it. In this sample he found no " little animals " and he surmised rightly enough that the previous sample of rain-water had become contaminated from the gutters of the house. Though he himself was unaware of it, van Leeuwenhoek had brought to light the first evidence against the theory of heterogenesis, or spontaneous generation, a theory which received its death-blow from the researches of Spallanzani. In spite of this, however, as we shall see, heterogenesis now threatens to rise again in a new form in relation to viruses.

At the time of Spallanzani's birth in 1729, the belief in spontaneous generation had already been assailed and Redi had shown by a simple experiment that maggots did not arise in meat if the parent fly was prevented from laying her eggs in it. Notwithstanding this, no one doubted that Leeuwenhoek's " little animals " arose spontaneously in any kind of broth if left long enough. Indeed an Englishman, Needham by name, claimed to have proved that micro-organisms were produced from broths even after careful heating, and put out a theory that there existed a " Vegetative Force " which could apparently give rise to any type of living organism at will. Luckily Spallanzani exploded this myth before it was generally accepted, and showed that the reason for the appearance of organisms in Needham's broths was the fact that he had not heated his concoctions sufficiently. Spallanzani proved that if the broth was properly heated, and protected from contamination after heating, no bacteria or other organisms appeared in it; in other words, the broth was sterile and remained sterile.

So far we have talked only of bacteria, and have hardly mentioned the viruses with which this book is solely concerned. It was Pasteur who, in his studies of rabies, first conceived the existence of something so excessively minute as a virus which, in spite of its size, was yet able to cause a serious disease and to multiply itself in the process.

We have seen previously how Spallanzani made his broth sterile by means of heat; but there is another method of sterilising a fluid and that is by removing mechanically all the micro-organisms from it. This can be done by forcing the fluid through a filter made of unglazed clay, the pores of which are too small to allow the passage of bacteria. In 1892 Iwanowsky, a Russian botanist, passed the sap from a tobacco plant, infected with a disease called "mosaic," through such a filter and obtained a filtrate free from all bacteria. On inoculating this filtrate to healthy tobacco plants he was astonished to find that the filtrate was still actively infectious. This was the first scientific proof of the existence of the "filterable viruses" as they came to be called. Iwanowsky's discovery, which seems to have caused little comment at the time, was reinvestigated a few years later by Beijerinck, who suggested that the causal agent of the tobacco mosaic disease was a living infectious fluid, "contagium vivum fluidum," as he called it.

After this came the work of Loeffler and Frosch, who, in one of the reports of the German commission which had been investigating the cause and cure of the foot-and-mouth disease of cattle, showed that the causal agent was still present even after the fluid had been passed through a bacteria-proof filter. They also showed that it could not be a simple poison, as it was capable of acting in great dilutions, greater than that of any known poison, and, what is more, was able to increase in amount when inoculated into a healthy animal, just as do the disease-causing bacteria.

About this time the so-called " germ-theory " of disease was still a subject for controversy among medical men, but after this was accepted, and the micro-organisms causing many infectious diseases had been identified, there still remained infectious disorders for which no causative organisms could be found. Among these were smallpox, mumps, chicken-pox, measles and many others, and it was thought for a long time that these were due to extremely small bacteria. Now we know that they are virus diseases, and that viruses attack practically every kind of living organism from bacteria themselves to man, whilst the plants alone are susceptible to attack by about 150 separate viruses.

Before we mention by name a few of the more important virus diseases, some of which are illustrated in this book, it is necessary to give one or two of the outstanding characteristics of the viruses as a group, and to point out some of the differences between them and the bacteria. In the first place, there is the extremely small size of viruses; all those which attack plants are, so far as we know at present, below the limit of vision with the optical microscope. The actual size and shape of viruses are dealt with in Chapter 9, p. 93. A few of the animal viruses, vaccinia, for example, can be seen by means of dark ground illumination. It is from this small size that the terms " filterable " and " ultra-microscopic " viruses are derived. Another important characteristic is the close association of viruses with living cells; no one has yet succeeded in cultivating a virus in a medium free from cells. It must have a living cell in which to multiply. Some viruses, apart from their disease-causing ability, are similar in most respects to some of the complex chemical substances found in all living tissues and, as we shall see later, they can be purified and crystallised. In this manner they differ from bacteria and our conception of what constitutes a living organism. On the other hand, they have some characteristics of living things, especially in their power to multiply and to mutate into closely similar forms. Another characteristic of viruses, which is shared to a lesser degree by other disease agents, is their relationship with insects, upon which many viruses depend for their transmission from host to host.

We have stated that all the major groups of living organisms are susceptible to attack by viruses and this is easily demonstrated by a brief glance at some of the more important virus diseases. Probably the first evidence of the existence of a virus-like agent which destroyed bacteria was obtained in 1894 by Hankin, who discovered that the waters of the Jumna and the Ganges had a bactericidal action on the cholera germ. He found that the water from the Ganges killed the cholera microbe in three hours. Filtering the water had no effect on this property, but boiling the water destroyed its bactericidal action. This is what would be expected if the water contained some agent of a virus-like nature. On the other hand, Hankin found that well-water, whether boiled or filtered, made a good medium for the cholera germ. In 1915 it was shown by Twort, and later by the Canadian, d'Herelle, that bacteria were liable to be attacked by some agent which dissolved them. The name given by d'Herelle to this agent was " *Bacteriophagum intestinale.*" Since then it has been shown that bacteria are liable to attack by a large number of these virus-like agents or bacteriophages, and they are now generally known as the bacterial viruses.

There is a special class of viruses which attacks insects, causing what are known as the polyhedral diseases, so-called because of the peculiar polyhedra which are found in vast numbers in the blood of infected insects. These viruses, which appear to attack only the larval forms of insects, must not be confused with the viruses which are carried by insects from one host to another. This is an entirely different relationship, no apparent disease being caused in the insect, as there is in the case of the polyhedral viruses.

Birds are very susceptible to virus infections, some of which belong to the related group known as the pox viruses. The domestic fowl is liable to attack by one of these, and an example is shown in the frontispice. Among the other viruses attacking fowls, particular interest attaches to those which produce cancers, the Rous sarcoma, for example. (See Chap. 7.) Fishes and frogs are sometimes infected with viruses, and a virus sarcoma is known to occur in the leopard-frog. Horses are susceptible to a mosquito-borne virus, and cattle to the well-known foot-and-mouth disease. Rabies and distemper attack dogs, whilst the list of viruses which attack man is very long.

Many viruses attack plants, producing malformations, growths and patterns on the foliage and flowers, and some cause the death of leaves and sometimes of the whole plant. The pretty patterns on the leaves of the variegated *Abutilon*, which used to be grown a lot in this country as an ornamental plant, are due to an insect-transmitted virus.

Up to about fifteen years ago progress in the study of viruses, as distinct from virus diseases, was slow, but after the isolation of tobacco mosaic virus by Stanley in 1935, the application of new techniques has greatly enlarged our knowledge of these agents. Many of the negative properties which were the criteria used to characterise viruses about a decade ago are now being replaced by more positive knowledge; for example, the viruses which were once said to be ultramicroscopic can now be examined in detail with the aid of the electron microscope, and many have been photographed. Some of these electron micrographs are reproduced in this book.

If we look back over the past, and examine how the study of the viruses has progressed, we can pick out a number of discoveries that are important events in the history of the subject. After each of these events, except perhaps the first, there has been a spurt of progress. The first of these milestones on the long road of discovery was the demonstration by Iwanowsky of the existence of a disease agent small enough to pass through bacteria-proof filters—in other words, the discovery of the first virus. Then followed the demonstration by Loeffler and Frosch that foot-and-mouth disease also belonged to the category of virus diseases. The next important discoveries were, perhaps, those of Carroll, who linked up the spread of yellow fever with the mosquito, and of Takata, who showed that the dwarf disease of rice was also spread by an insect. These discoveries opened a new chapter in virus research, for the relationship between viruses and their insect vectors is of very great importance, and is far from being completely understood.

For a long time after these discoveries, attention was mainly directed towards the virus disease, and the virus itself was regarded as a mysterious something whose existence could only be deduced from the disease it caused. After the first isolation of a virus, which was the next great step forward, it was possible to recognise viruses as tangible entities, and progress became rapid. Stanley's isolation of tobacco mosaic virus as paracrystals, or " liquid crystals," was followed by the work of Bawden and Pirie, who showed that the virus of tomato bushy stunt would crystallise into rhombic dodecahedra, true three-dimensional crystals. Altogether five or six plant viruses have now been isolated in crystalline form, and these are dealt with in Chapter 9. At the time of writing, no animal virus has been crystallised.

Another important step forward has been the successful growing of some viruses by tissue-culture methods. Whilst it is true enough that viruses will only grow inside a living cell, nothing prevents the cell being detached from the main organism and grown in a culture medium, since it is the cell which is the nurse to the virus and not the whole organism. From this method of tissue culture have been developed some important methods of combating human virus diseases.

The reader is now, perhaps, in a better position to understand what this book is about, and it may help to recapitulate some of the main facts which have been discovered about the viruses. All viruses are extremely small. Most of the animal and probably all the plant viruses are below the limit of vision with the optical microscope; some plant viruses are almost of molecular size. Unlike most bacteria and microscopic fungi, viruses cannot be cultivated in a cell-free medium; they can only multiply in a living cell and all cause disease in some form or other. Many viruses have a close relationship with the insects which transmit them and they are entirely dependent upon these insects to carry them from host to host. Viruses appear to be obligate parasites, and free-existing viruses probably do not occur. Although minute bacteria of the size of some of the larger viruses have been found in sewage, there is no evidence of any direct relationship between these and viruses. In spite of the considerable progress made in the study of viruses generally, we still have much to learn about their mode of multiplication and reproduction.

CHAPTER 2

HOW VIRUSES GET ABOUT

WE HAVE SEEN in our discussions of various virus diseases that viruses are infectious and must therefore spread from diseased to healthy organisms, but we have not yet investigated the methods by which viruses are spread around. These, as we shall see, are very varied but, on the whole, rather different from the modes of dispersal of visible disease agents. The main point of difference is the dependence of many viruses, affecting both plants and animals, upon some other agent to transmit them. This other agent is usually an insect which preys upon the host of the virus in question, and the obvious example of this type of transmission is the spread of yellow fever by certain species of mosquito. Since the subject of this insect-virus partnership is an interesting and complicated one, we have dealt with it separately in the next chapter and for the moment are only concerned with other methods of virus dispersal.

Plant viruses can be spread in a variety of ways, apart from the agency of insects, but it seems necessary for a wound, however slight, to be made in the tissues of a susceptible plant before a virus can enter. The following are the methods by which plant viruses are transmitted (*a*) by contact between diseased and healthy plants; (*b*) by inoculation; (*c*) by grafting; (*d*) by seed; (*e*) by vegetative propagation; (*f*) through the soil. Note that all but (*b*) are natural methods.

Not many plant viruses spread through contact of plants in the field, and those that do occur in high concentration in the sap of the infected plant. This is understandable enough, since the amount of sap transferred from one plant to another in the process of knocking against each other in the field must be extremely minute. This method of spread, however, is of considerable economic importance since a very common potato virus, the cause of mild mosaic, is transmitted in this way. Moreover, it has recently been demonstrated that the virus can also be transmitted by underground contact by way of roots. Another common virus which can spread by contact between leaves is that of tobacco mosaic, the most infectious plant virus known but one which curiously enough is not, so far as we know, transmitted in nature by insects.

The next method of spread is really the artificial counterpart of spread by contact since inoculation consists in rubbing sap from a virus-diseased plant on to the leaves of a healthy susceptible one. The sap is extracted from the diseased leaves by pounding them in a sterile mortar and is then gently rubbed over the surface of the healthy leaf with the finger or a glass spatula with a ground glass face. Transmission of the virus is made more effective by some substance, such as carborundum powder, which will act as an abrasive. By this means numerous slight wounds are made in the leaf epidermis, thus allowing more entrance points for the virus. It must be emphasised, however, that the rubbing should be gentle since a virus can only multiply inside a living cell, and if the cells are killed by a too vigorous rubbing the first essential for virus multiplication is lost.

All viruses which are systemic in their hosts are transmissible by grafting; the usual method for herbaceous plants being the cleft-graft, in which the scion is pared to a wedge shape and inserted in a vertical slit cut in the stem of the stock (Fig. 9, p. 143). The whole is then bound together with rubber tape and finished with a drop of rubber solution. When organic union is made, the rubber tape is removed or perishes. Grafting is of course an artificial method of virus transmission, but there is an interesting example of natural transmission by means of the parasitic plant, dodder (*Cuscuta* spp.), which amounts to a kind of natural graft. The dodder plant has turned out to be a useful tool in the hands of the virus worker because it enables certain viruses to be studied in new and more convenient host plants. For example, by this means, a virus from the cranberry has been transmitted to such plants as tomato and tobacco. This could not be effected in any other way since it is not possible to graft the cranberry to tomato or tobacco plants, and the virus, which cannot be transmitted by sap-inoculation, has a specific insect vector which will not feed on those two plants. This technique of course is limited in its application by two factors, the host range of the parasitic dodder and its susceptibility to the virus under investigation.

It is a curious fact that very few plant viruses are carried in the seed; various explanations for this have been put forward, the most plausible being the anatomical isolation of the embryo, but we have, at present, very little exact knowledge of the subject.

A few viruses are seed-transmitted, the best known being those of bean mosaic and lettuce mosaic. In contrast to this, infrequent transmission by seed is the almost invariable spread of infection by means of vegetative propagation from a virus-diseased plant.

Provided the virus is systemic in its host plant, tubers, bulbs, cuttings, runners, rhizomes, etc., from a virus-infected plant give rise in turn to similarly diseased plants. It is for this reason that virus diseases are of such paramount importance in crops like potatoes, flower bulbs, many perennial flowers, raspberries, strawberries and hops, all of which are vegetatively propagated.

There are one or two examples known of transmission of viruses through the soil, those of tobacco necrosis and wheat rosette, for example. In the first case the virus is carried in the water to the soil or floats on to it from the air in fragments of dried infected leaf tissue. Once in the soil, it enters the roots by the minute wounds made by the breaking of the hairs as the root moves through the soil. An experiment made with this virus provides an interesting illustration of the important part played by wounding in plant virus infection. If young tobacco plants are grown in a water culture containing a solution of the virus, the roots do not become infected provided no accidental wounding to the roots has occurred. But if similar plants are grown in soil or sand, to which virus solution has been added, the virus invariably enters the roots by way of the hairs which are broken off as the roots make their way through the soil.

The other case of soil transmission, that of wheat rosette, is more mysterious and the mechanism of infection is not known. The soil remains infectious to wheat plants for a period of years once rosetted wheat has been grown in it. Heating such soil or treating it with formaldehyde or other disinfectants renders it non-effective, but no soil insect or other organism has been found capable of transmitting the virus. Since wheat plants cannot be infected by sap-inoculation or only with very great difficulty, it is not easy to see how soil-transmission of this virus takes place.

Having briefly outlined the methods of dispersal of plant viruses, it is necessary to point out that the viruses vary greatly in their transmissibility. As already stated, all viruses which are uniformly distributed throughout the plant are transmissible by grafting, but apart from this we find all grades of infectivity. Many of the mosaic type viruses are transmissible by mechanical sap-inoculation, and in the field are spread by a particular insect or group of similar insects. Other virus diseases cannot be spread by mechanical methods and are entirely dependent upon a specific insect vector; whilst a third group of viruses apparently do not spread at all in nature, or, if they do, we have no knowledge of the method. Most of these viruses are transmissible by mechanical sap-inoculation, but this is not a natural method of spread. Outstanding in this group is the so-called paracrinkle virus of " King Edward " potatoes. *All* potato plants of this variety, together with the mutant " Red King," in whatever part of the world they may occur, contain a virus. This virus can be transmitted mechanically to other potato plants and to tomatoes, but no insect vector has been found and the virus has never been known to occur naturally in any other potato variety or other plant besides the " King Edward " potato. It does not appear to produce any disease or abnormal appearance in this variety, and the only way its presence can be determined is to graft a scion to another susceptible potato variety or inoculate by sap. In the potato " Arran Victory " transmission by grafting or inoculation from " King Edward " potatoes produces a severe distorting disease which can then be passed on indefinitely to other " Arran Victory " potato plants. The puzzle then is to explain the infection of the first " King Edward " seedling (and it apparently was a seedling) with a virus which does not seem to spread in nature. Other viruses in this group of which the method of spread has never been discovered are tomato bushy stunt virus, which can be seen in its crystalline form in P. IV p. 53 and tomato black-ring virus. In addition to these are viruses which, for want of a better description, may be called " laboratory viruses." These have been found infecting single plants and no natural mode of spread has been discovered. Such viruses have only been recorded once and would have disappeared on the death of the original host plant had they not been propagated artificially in the laboratory. Examples of these are the viruses of broken ringspot, *Arabis* mosaic, lovage mosaic and the black ring virus of tomatoes.

Transmission of animal viruses, like that of plant viruses, occurs in various ways, and insects, too, play their part. A common mode of transmission is by way of the respiratory tract by droplet infection, and the viruses of measles, influenza and the common cold are all spread in this way.

The virus of foot-and-mouth disease is one of the most infectious viruses known, and the disease is spread whenever an infected animal comes into contact with a healthy one, probably by droplets in the breath. The more common method of infection is indirect transmission by means of contaminated material of all kinds, the excretion of infected animals, soiled straw, contaminated drinking water, yards, pastures and highways, and by the men working on and around the farm.

Fowl-pox is an eruptive disease which attacks pigeons and fowls (see Frontispiece), and in its mode of transmission we see an interesting parallel to the spread of the tobacco necrosis virus. In the latter case it will be remembered that tobacco plants growing in a liquid medium containing virus solution did not become infected, but if they were growing in soil or sand which contained the virus they did. This was because during passage of the roots through the soil, the root hairs were broken and entry was thus afforded to the virus. Fowl-pox also spreads by contact but apparently a slight wound is essential to allow the virus to enter. This can be demonstrated by the following simple experiment: When virus is added to the drinking water of pigeons no infection results, but if a small quantity of sharp grit is added at the same time then the pigeons do become infected. The slight abrasions made by the grit while the birds are drinking allow the virus to gain an entry.

In the next chapter we have discussed the relationship of viruses and their insect vectors at some length, but there are some animals, other than insects, which are concerned with the spread of viruses and they may be appropriately discussed here. Everybody knows of the virus disease of rabies and how it is transmitted to other animals, including man, by the bite of a rabid dog. This virus is spread only by the bite of an infected animal, the virus being thereby introduced into the nerve fibres torn by the bite. It is interesting to note, in passing, that recently a new vector of rabies has appeared on the scene. This new vector is a bat, a blood-sucking or vampire bat, and it has been responsible for an epidemic of rabies, mostly in South America and Trinidad, where it infected cattle and a number of human beings.

The virus of influenza is not confined to man but attacks also such animals as the ferret and the pig, and it was during investigation of hog influenza that a very curious and interesting relationship of this virus with a most unexpected type of animal was brought to light (Shope, 1941). One of the puzzling facts about influenza in pigs was the way in which isolated animals suddenly developed the disease without any apparent contact with a source of infection. Now there is a belief among farmers in some of the middle western states of the U.S.A. that earthworms have something to do with another virus disease of pigs that we call swine fever. So this directed the attention of investigators to the earthworm as a possible link in the influenza cycle. Now it may seem unlikely that the earthworm could have anything to do with influenza, but there are two facts here which are significant. First, earthworms are frequently eaten by pigs, and secondly the earthworm is the alternative host for another type of worm, a parasitic worm which spends part of its life in the earthworm and part in the lungs of the pig. Before we go on to consider the part played by these worms in the spread of hog influenza it will be necessary to digress for a moment and describe very briefly the life cycle of the lungworm. The eggs are deposited in the lungs of the pig by the female lungworm, and these are coughed up by the pig and swallowed, eventually passing out with the faeces. The eggs are then swallowed by an earthworm in which they hatch into first-stage larvae. Two further developmental stages are passed in the earthworm, and the larvae are then in the third stage and ready to infect the pig. At this stage the larvae are localised in large numbers in the heart, gizzard and certain glands of the earthworm, and here they must wait until they are swallowed by a pig. If necessary the larvae are capable of waiting for this in the third stage as long as four years.

When the earthworm is eventually swallowed by a pig, the lungworm larvae become liberated in the intestines of the animal. They next bore through the walls of the intestine and make their way to the lungs, where they undergo two more developmental changes, finally becoming adult lungworms.

The next step was to show that the lungworm actually harboured the influenza virus. Not only does it do this, but it is capable of retaining it for as long as two years. Apparently, however, the virus in the lungworm is present in a masked non-infective form, and in order to produce infection some provocative stimulus must be applied to the swine it infects. This can be brought about by intramuscular injections of certain bacteria, *Haemophilus influenzae suis*.

Some of the most infectious animal viruses are those which attack insects; by this we mean the actual virus diseases of insects and not the insect vector and the virus it transmits, a relationship which we discuss in the next chapter. Some insect virus diseases are known as the polyhedral diseases because of the characteristic crystalline polyhedral bodies associated with the disease; others are known as wilts, jaundice, etc. A peculiarity of these diseases is that they appear to attack only the larval and sometimes the pupal stages, but never the adult insect.

The most probable method of transmission of these caterpillar wilts is through the mouth, i.e. by eating contaminated foliage, but little work has been carried out on the subject. It is not very clear how these insect viruses over-winter, but it is thought that a percentage of infected larvae do not die but complete their metamorphosis and thus transmit the virus through the eggs to the next generation. (See Chap. 7, p. 68.)

Reference

SHOPE, R. E. (1941). The swine lungworm as a reservoir and intermediate host for swine influenza virus. *J. Exp. Med.* 74: 49-68.

CHAPTER 3

THE INSECT-VIRUS PARTNERSHIP

IN THE PREVIOUS chapter we have read something of how viruses are spread about. Some, like influenza, are spread by an infected person sneezing or coughing; droplet infection as it is called. Others are so infectious that they can be spread by contact between diseased and healthy organisms; foot-and-mouth disease of cattle, for example. But many other viruses cannot be spread in this way. When yellow fever was rampant in Cuba in 1900, an American Military Mission under Walter Reed was sent out to investigate the epidemic. One of the first things to find out was how the disease was spread and very careful experiments were made to this end. There were no guinea pigs or other laboratory animals available for this virus in those days, so that human volunteers had to be used instead. These were forthcoming, as always, and attempts were made to infect them with yellow fever by giving them the pyjamas of yellow fever patients and by allowing them to sleep in the beds in which patients had died. However, none of the volunteers was infected in this way. In the meantime a Cuban doctor, Carlos Findlay, had been proclaiming to an unheeding world that yellow fever was caused by a mosquito and it had been noticed by the Military Mission that outbreaks of the disease occurred in a curiously spasmodic fashion. One family might become infected in one house whilst the next attack might be some distance away in the next street. In fact, it looked as if an insect *was* carrying the disease. More volunteers were therefore confined in a special hut which was provided with clean bed-linen, etc., but into which a number of mosquitoes were introduced which had fed

on a yellow fever patient. In due course some of these volunteers
developed yellow fever and other experiments confirmed that
the mosquito was the actual carrier, or vector, of the disease. At
the time of those experiments it was not known that yellow fever
was due to a virus; that discovery followed at a later date. At
about the same time workers at the Imperial Agricultural
Experiment Station in Japan had the impression that a certain
type of sap-sucking insect, a leaf-hopper, was connected in some
way with a disease of the rice plant known as " dwarf." They
however, were under the impression that the insects themselves
were the cause of the disease, and it was not until some years
later that it was shown that the insects were carrying something
which caused the disease.

Now we know that there has evolved a close relationship
between insects and viruses, especially plant viruses, and that
this relationship is both interesting and complicated. If we
examine the various insects which have been found capable of
transmitting viruses we find that they are mostly insects of a
special type, i.e. insects which feed in a particular manner. The
large order known as the Hemiptera contains many different
kinds of insects, but they all have this in common, that they
possess sucking mouth-parts and so feed only on the juices of
their host. The Hemiptera contains many well-known insects
such as the aphids, or greenfly, and the leaf-hoppers, and these
are the insects which are concerned with the transmission of
many plant viruses.

If we examine the mouth-parts of one of these insects we
shall understand, perhaps, one reason why such insects are
efficient transmitters of viruses. As will be seen later, however,
the method of feeding of insects is by no means the whole
explanation of insect-virus relationship; it merely suggests why
such insects are suitable vectors.

In an Hemipterous insect the mouth-parts consist of a long
tubular beak or rostrum, the *labium*, which, however, is not the
actual piercing organ. It acts as a supporting structure for two
pairs of fine needles, the mandibles and maxillae, which slide
within it. On the inner face of the maxillae are two grooves, and

when these come together they form two fine canals down one of which flows saliva from the salivary glands and up the other flows a mixture of sap and saliva drawn up by the strong pharyngeal pump situated in the head. The maxillae and the mandibles fit tightly together and both slide in the enveloping beak or labium. When the insect feeds it presses the tip of the labium on the leaf and the labium bends and becomes fore-shortened, the stylets being driven into the plant tissue (see Plate XVI, p. 128). Now it is perhaps clearer why such insects are suitable for inoculating viruses into plants. If the host plant is infected with a virus, the latter is drawn up with the sap into the stomach of the insect; from there it passes out into the blood and thence to the salivary glands. Then when the insect feeds on a healthy, susceptible plant the virus is pumped down with the saliva and injected into the plant. The advantages of this method for virus infection are fairly obvious; the virus is intro-duced directly into the living cells with the minimum of injury to the cells, and, furthermore, the type of tissue, the vascular bundles, which most sucking insects prefer, is also the most suitable for the multiplication of the virus and its distribution throughout the plant.

However, as we have already said, the situation is not as simple as that ; every sucking insect which feeds upon a virus-infected plant is not necessarily capable of transmitting the virus to a healthy plant. For example, there is one large group of sap-sucking insects, the Capsidae, which are apparently unable to transmit any plant viruses. We do not really know why this is, though we can perhaps hazard a guess. One of the main char-acteristics of a virus is the necessity for it to have a living cell in which to multiply, and this primary need is not filled under the conditions of the capsid's feeding. This insect's saliva is poisonous to the plant cells, so that the virus, supposing it to be present, is introduced into tissue composed of dead and dying cells.

A question the reader may be inclined to ask here is, why does not any kind of plant-feeding insect carry plant viruses, merely by the contamination of its jaws? All we can say in answer to that is, that we don't know. To this question we can add another: why are not all plant viruses carried by insects?

The question of the transmission of virus by mechanical contamination of the insect's mouth-parts is an interesting one if only for the fact that it apparently does not occur. There is the case of tobacco mosaic virus, the most infectious plant virus known, which does not seem to have any natural insect vector.

We have stated that the great majority of plant viruses are of carried by sap-sucking insects, but the recently discovered virus turnip yellow mosaic (Frontispiece) is transmitted only by biting insects, and this, on the face of it, would appear to be a case of mechanical contamination of the jaws, but the experimental evidence suggests that this is not the case.

Although we cannot yet answer the question why all plant viruses are not carried by insects, we can perhaps throw a little light on the subject by examining some of the different types of relationship between insects and viruses, and, if in our survey we include some of the animal viruses, it is possible to find every type of relationship from the case where a virus is only just transmitted by the insect to that where there is a fundamental connection between the two.

The mechanical transmission of a virus by the accidental contamination of the jaws would obviously constitute the simplest relationship between virus and insect. In the animal viruses the nearest approach would be the transmission of typhus fever by the louse or possibly of poliomyelitis by flies. There is some doubt as to the exact method of infection in the case of typhus, but it is thought to take place through the contaminated faeces of the louse becoming scratched into the skin by the victim. Typhus fever is probably a virus (or rickettsia) disease of insects in the first place, and man has become a secondary host at a later stage. There seems to be no authentic case of true mechanical transmission of a plant virus by an insect unless it be the transmission of cucumber mosaic virus by the cucumber beetle recorded only in America. There is, however, a group of aphis-transmitted plant viruses, known as the *non-persistent* viruses, where the connection between aphid and virus is relatively tenuous. For example, the insect picks up the virus after a very short period of feeding on the source but loses it again very rapidly. Usually after feeding for a short time on a healthy plant it is no longer infectious if transferred to a second healthy plant. Moreover, it has been shown that the aphids retain infectivity longer if they are starved immediately after feeding on the source of virus than if they are placed directly on a healthy plant. This suggests that the virus is rapidly digested by the insect, and the fact that the aphid remains infectious longer if starved is probably due to the reduction in the flow of digestive enzymes.

In contrast to the non-persistent viruses, there are the so-called *persistent* viruses; these are retained by the insect for long periods, frequently for the rest of its life, without necessity for recourse to a fresh supply of virus. Such persistent viruses, in contrast to the non-persistent, are as a rule not transmissible by mechanical methods.

An interesting point in the insect-virus partnership is the evolution of a relationship between different viruses and different types of insects. Thus, instead of a virus being carried by only one species of insect, it may be transmitted by quite a number of species, but they are all closely related. Potato leafroll virus, for example, can be spread by several different kinds of aphids but not by any of the other sap-sucking insects such as capsid bugs and leaf-hoppers which also infest the potato crops. On the other hand, a virus may be spread by as many as fifty different kinds of leaf-hoppers, but aphids are quite unable to transmit it. The curly-top virus of sugar-beet is spread by a leaf-hopper, and although aphids will feed on infected sugar-beet plants and will imbibe the virus which can be detected in the blood, they still are unable to spread the virus. In one case of a plant virus, however, this kind of group specificity does break down. Turnip yellow mosaic virus is transmitted in nature by a flea beetle, an insect with biting mouth-parts. Experimentally, however, the virus can be carried by a variety of quite unrelated insects, beetle larvae, grasshoppers and earwigs, but all attempts to make sucking insects spread the virus have failed. Now although the group specificity admittedly breaks down here, all insects which do transmit the virus must conform in one respect; they must have biting mouth-parts. Moreover, there is some evidence which suggests (it is not more than a suggestion at present) that to be a vector of this virus the insect must lack salivary glands. This may appear, at first sight, a peculiar qualification for virus transmission, especially as it has been pointed out previously that the salivary glands play an important part in the transmission of plant viruses by sucking insects. However, the explanation seems to lie in the fact that insects lacking salivary glands aid their digestion of the leaf-tissue by regurgitation of the contents of the forepart of the gut, during mastication of the leaf.

In so doing, virus-infected tissue which had been previously eaten would come into contact with the leaves of the healthy plant. This would also explain the fact that beetles which have fed on a plant infected with the turnip yellow mosaic virus do not become immediately infective to a healthy plant as they should if the virus was being carried mechanically on the jaws (Markham and Smith, 1949).

It is an interesting question whether insects are themselves affected in any way by the viruses they transmit; we know that the louse is killed by the typhus virus or rickettsiae, but then, as already mentioned, typhus is thought to have been a disease of insects in the first place. So far as we know, however, plant viruses have no adverse effect upon their insect vectors.

Quite a number of experiments have been carried out on the relationship between insects and viruses and a good deal of interesting information has been obtained. We have seen how some viruses of the non-persistent type are carried for only a short period by the insect, whilst others—persistent—may be carried for the remainder of the insect's life. Now by juggling with the time-relationships between insect and virus it has been found possible to show that certain plant virus diseases are composite in nature and to isolate the separate viruses by varying the time of feeding of the insect. This can be illustrated by the virus disease of strawberries known as " yellow-edge." If the strawberry aphid is allowed to feed for several days on an infected strawberry plant and then transferred for twenty-four hours to healthy plants of *Fragaria vesca*, which is used as a kind of *indicator* plant, these plants develop a mild virus disease. Now, if the same aphids, after feeding for twenty-four hours on the first lot of *F. vesca* plants, are transferred again to a second batch of healthy *F. vesca* plants, a mild virus disease of a different type from the first develops on these plants too. The explanation of this phenomenon lies in the time relationships between virus and insect. Both viruses are picked up by the aphid during its long feed on the strawberry plant infected with yellow edge, and one virus is transmitted to the first lot of *F. vesca* plants during the first twenty-four-hour feed. Since this virus is rapidly lost by the aphid, not persisting for more than an hour or two in the body of the insect, it is transmitted only to the first batch of *F. vesca* plants. But the second virus which is of the persistent type, has a delay of twenty-four hours or more in the body of the insect before it becomes infective, and so it is transmitted only to the second batch of plants. Thus it is possible, by varying the feeding times of the aphid, not only to show that a virus disease may be a composite one, but also to separate out the component viruses (Prentice, 1948).

Sometimes a plant virus disease may be caused by two viruses of which only one is insect-transmitted, and here again the insect may be employed to demonstrate the composite nature of the disease. Thus in certain virus diseases of the potato plant a different disease may be produced in the healthy host plant, according to whether the plant is infected by means of the aphid or by sap-inoculation.

The explanation is that the aphid selects from the composite disease the virus it transmits, leaving the other behind, and the single virus thus selected produces a different reaction from that due to the two viruses which are both transmitted by mechanical inoculation.

It is sometimes possible by means of a small surgical operation to convert a non-vector insect into a vector so far as a particular virus is concerned. This has been done with a leaf-hopper, which transmits a virus disease of maize in Africa. It was discovered that there exist two races of the same species of leaf-hopper, one race being able to transmit the virus and the other unable to do so. Actually the two types of insects looked identical and no difference could be detected between them. However, if a puncture was made with a fine needle, through the wall of the intestine of the insects which could not transmit the virus, they became vectors so long as the puncture remained open. This suggests that there is some property of the wall of the alimentary canal in the non-vector type which prevents the virus from passing through and reaching the blood, an essential preliminary to virus transmission in sucking insects (Storey, 1932).

Leaf-hoppers are insects which can withstand a surprising amount of maltreatment, and this hardiness renders them very suitable for experimental purposes. Besides the surgical operation just described, they have also been subjected to high temperatures, and when the insects have been carrying a virus this has had rather an unexpected result. If leaf-hoppers, infected with the virus of aster yellows, are exposed to high temperatures for a long period, they lose the power to infect healthy plants unless they are allowed to feed once more on a source of virus. If, however, the insects are heated for a shorter period, they also lose the power to infect, but regain it after an interval (Kunkel, 1937). One interpretation of this phenomenon is that the prolonged heating of the insect destroyed all the virus in its body, but that the shorter period reduced the amount below the threshold of infection, which was regained after a lapse of time by multiplication of the virus inside the insect. This question of the multiplication of plant viruses within the body of the transmitting insect is a vexed one, and it is by no means sure that multiplication of plant viruses does take place inside the insect vectors, although some recent work suggests that it does so in some cases. In this connection it may be of interest to compare the behaviour of an animal virus and a plant virus within the bodies of the insect vectors when subjected to low temperatures. The viruses concerned are those of yellow fever and aster yellows, and the insects are a mosquito and a leaf-hopper respectively. To take the plant virus first, it is a characteristic of the persistent viruses to which we have referred earlier in this chapter, that they do not become infective at once, but there is usually a delay in the development of infective power, which in the case of aster yellows is as much as nine days. But nine days is longer than the nymphal life of the leaf-hopper, and therefore the nymphs are unable to transmit the virus, but only do so after they have turned into adults. If, however, such nymphs are exposed to low temperatures, the larval development is retarded, but not the development of infective power. Under these conditions the nymphs will transmit the virus. Now compare the case of the mosquito and the yellow fever virus. The delay in development of infective power in the mosquito at a given temperature is about the same as with the leaf-hopper, i.e. nine days; but if the mosquito is subjected to low temperatures the delay in the development of infective power, unlike that of the leaf-hopper, is also prolonged. This seems to indicate a fundamental difference between the two, and to suggest that the yellow fever virus is much more intimately bound up with the metabolism of the mosquito itself than is the aster yellows virus with the metabolism of the leaf-hopper. Further support for this is indicated by the fact that the yellow fever virus is known to multiply inside the mosquito's body.

An important point in the relationship between viruses and their insect vectors is the question of the inheritance of a virus by the progeny of virus-carrying (viruliferous) insects. This, as we shall see, is bound up with the question we have just been discussing, the multiplication of a plant virus in its insect vector. The passing of a virus from a parent insect to its progeny is a rare occurrence, but before we discuss the matter further, it is necessary to point out that we are only concerned here with viruses which are carried by insect vectors and not with virus diseases of insects, dealt with in Chapter 6 (p. 56), which are also passed from parent to offspring. It is necessary, therefore, for the reader, at this point, to differentiate clearly in his own mind between a virus which attacks a plant or an animal and which is carried by an insect vector, and a virus which attacks the insect itself and produces a fatal disease in that insect.

To return now to the question of the inheritance of a plant virus by the progeny of a viruliferous insect vector, there are only two authentic cases known of this, and they are both viruses carried by leap-hoppers. The first is the " dwarf disease " of rice, which has been studied by Fukushi (1939) in Japan. He showed that the virus was passed from parent to offspring to the third generation without recourse to a fresh source of virus. For the virus to be inherited by the progeny it was necessary for the female parent to be infective; if only the male parent was infected the offspring were all virus-free.

The fact that the virus was apparently passed to the third generation is highly suggestive that multiplication of the virus had taken place inside the insect. However, more convincing evidence on this point has recently been presented by Black (1950), who has worked with a virus causing a disease of clover called " club leaf." This virus, like that of dwarf disease of rice, has a specific insect vector, the leaf-hopper *Agalliopsis novella* (Say.), and cannot be transmitted by mechanical means. The virus is passed from the female parent to the offspring, as is shown by the following experiments carried out by Black. Virus-bearing females of the leaf-hopper were caged on lucerne plants (alfalfa), which is immune to the virus. Thirty nymphs were removed from the lucerne plants as they hatched from the eggs deposited by the insects, care being taken that they did not feed on the plants in which the eggs had been laid. Each nymph was placed on a crimson clover seedling, *Trifolium incarnatum*, which is susceptible to the virus, and transferred at weekly intervals to a fresh seedling till it died. None of the clover seedlings kept as controls became infected, but 68 out of 642 of the test plants did. These 68 plants were infected, by 24 of the 27 insects which survived more than two weeks. None of the 24 insects infected plants until at least three weeks had elapsed from the time of hatching. This experiment proves that the virus is passed from the parent insect to its offspring.

Black's next experiment gives convincing proof that the virus must multiply in the insect. On 8 February 1945, a virus-bearing female leaf-hopper was mated with a virus-free male and the pair caged on a lucerne plant. The lucerne plant was grown in soil which had been steamed to kill weeds. The female produced

42 nymphs of which 21 were tested individually on a series of four crimson clover plants and then discarded. Fifteen of the 21 produced infections. Therefore, on the average, the virus in the original female had been diluted approximately 1-30 among her progeny. The 21 remaining progeny were each placed on a lucerne seedling and, when they became adults, the females were mated to virus-free males. The family with the greatest number of progeny was chosen for the main line of descent, and four supplementary families with more progeny than others were held in reserve. Black continued this experiment for more than five years through 21 generations of insects grown only on immune lucerne plants without loss of infectivity. If no multiplication of virus had taken place during this period, it has been calculated that the dilution of the original virus would exceed $2\cdot8 \times 10^{26}$, which, of course, is impossible.

Some of the implications of this work are interesting. If a plant virus is able to multiply inside an insect, then it becomes to a certain extent an animal virus also, and so bridges the gap between the two types of virus. It may be that other leaf-hopper-transmitted viruses also multiply in their insect vectors, and if this is the case the long " incubation period," so-called, of the virus in the heaf-hopper vector, before the insect becomes capable of transmission, may in truth be a period of preliminary multiplication of the virus.

It has been suggested that rickettsial diseases like typhus were originally diseases of insects which have become adapted to a vertebrate host, so that one could speculate whether the leaf-hopper-transmitted plant viruses may not also have been originally insect viruses which have become adapted to plants.

References

BLACK, L. M. (1950). A plant virus that multiplies in its insect vector. *Nature, London, 166*: 852-53.

FUKUSHI, T. (1939). Retention of virus by its insect vector through several generations. *Proc. Imp. Acad. Japan, 15*: 142-45.

KUNKEL, L. O. (1937). Effect of heat on ability of *Cicadula sexnotata* (*Fall.*) to transmit aster yellows. *Amer. J. Bot. 24*: 316-27.

MARKHAM, R., and SMITH, KENNETH M. (1949). Studies on the virus of turnip yellow mosaic. *Parasitology, 39* : 330-42.

PRENTICE, IAN W. (1948). Resolution of strawberry virus complexes. *Ann. Appl. Biol., 35*: 279-89.

STOREY, H. H. (1932). The inheritance by an insect vector of the ability to transmit a plant virus. *Proc. Roy. Soc. (B.) 112*: 46-60.

CHAPTER 4

THE GARDEN

WE HAVE SEEN how many plant viruses get about and also learned something about the relationships between viruses and insects, but so far nothing has been said of what a virus-diseased plant looks like. Actually there is no definite criterion of a virus disease which enables an observer to conclude from appearance alone that a particular disease is caused by a virus. In some cases, however, there are symptoms which are more suggestive of viruses than of other causes of disease, mottling of the leaves and changes in flower colour, for example. Now the reactions of plants in general to different virus infections are extremely varied and seem to cover every response a plant could reasonably be expected to make. One of the most characteristic symptoms is the mottling, already referred to, or *mosaic*, as it is usually called. This term was first used in 1886 by Mayer to describe the yellow and green mottlings on the leaves of tobacco plants, infected with the first virus to be described, because of a more or less fanciful resemblance of the mottlings to a mosaic pattern. This tobacco disease, then, was called *tobacco mosaic* and all mottling diseases of plants caused by viruses are now known as *mosaic diseases*.

The term mosaic in modern usage is rather an elastic one and covers a number of other symptoms which can hardly be called mottling. This confusion of nomenclature is partly due to the fact that a virus which causes leaf mottling on one host plant may give rise to quite a different symptom on another susceptible plant species.

A curious modification of the mosaic type of symptom is the

development on the leaves of numerous concentric rings usually with a central spot. Sometimes there may be as many as six or seven rings concentrically placed. These viruses are usually called ringspot viruses and there are about a dozen of them known (Plate Ib, p. 36).

Among the paintings of tulips dating from about the time of Rembrandt are some which show an attractive variegation of the petals and also a striping of the leaves. Many years later, such tulips were to fetch high prices because of the mistaken impression that they were rare mutations of a self-coloured variety. A reproduction of a woodcut of tulips attributed to Rabel and dating from about 1622 shows this colour change. In the frontispiece can be seen a modern illustration of the same colour change or " tulip break," as it is now called. We may therefore look upon " tulip break " as the oldest plant virus disease known, but of course no one at that time knew it was a disease or had any conception even of the existence of pathogenic bacteria, to say nothing of viruses. The first suggestion that the tulip break might be due to a disease was made much later.

Flower colour breaks, such as that in tulips, are a common symptom of mosaic diseases and sometimes give rise to quite attractive colour schemes although the plants are almost always slightly stunted.

Among the colour breaks occurring in garden plants, the most common, apart from tulips, are those in wallflowers (Frontispiece) and stocks, though breaks also occur in gladioli, pansies, anemones, poppies and one or two others. We shall have more to say about these symptoms later on.

Another type of response by certain virus-infected plants may be grouped together as distortions. These consist of several kinds; for example in one disease the veins of the leaves are twisted; this leads to a very distorted plant with the leaves sometimes looped over with the under-surface uppermost.

A common virus which attacks tomatoes, among other plants, has the effect of suppressing the leaf blade so that some of the leaves are represented by thin tendrils or " shoe-strings," as they are sometimes called. A strain of the tobacco mosaic virus also has this effect on tomatoes to an even greater degree, causing in addition outgrowths on the leaves and curious distortions.

There are two types of outgrowths caused in plants by viruses; one of these is known as an " enation " and consists of a complete miniature leaf in reverse growing on the underside of the normal leaf (Plate II, p. 37). Several viruses are known to have this effect, two of them being the type tobacco virus and one of its strains. The type virus, curiously enough, only produces these outgrowths on a particular species of plant, *Nicotiana paniculata*, but the strain produces them on a variety of hosts and is known as " enation mosaic " virus.

The second type of outgrowth is less common and is much more analogous to the virus tumours caused in animals. Unlike the enation, this kind of outgrowth is not organised in any way, but consists of a mass of undifferentiated cells. This virus, which chiefly attacks clover, is known as the " wound tumour " virus (Plate III, p. 52) because the tumours seem to form mainly at the site of any small injury to the stem or root.

From the point of view of garden plants, including hot-house plants, there are two viruses which occur most commonly and do most damage. These are the viruses of *cucumber mosaic* and *tomato spotted wilt*; both these have a wide host range and so are liable to attack many miscellaneous kinds of plants. The first virus is spread around by various species of aphids, but the second is carried only by a thrips and not by aphids or any other kind of insect. It is the only virus known to be transmitted by this kind of insect. The plants which suffer most in the garden from the attacks of cucumber mosaic virus are, as might be expected, the cucumber, whether of the outdoor ridge type, or the frame cucumber, and the vegetable marrow, although, of course, since the cucumber is an annual plant, infection must always come from outside. The first sign of attack is the development of small yellow spots and patches on the youngest leaves, accompanied by some yellowing of the veins. The yellow patches spread to the other leaves, which become distorted and stunted; the fruit is often misshapen and may show a mottling also. In the outdoor cucumber and the vegetable marrow the disease is a very serious one, and affected plants usually die prematurely or remain in a moribund condition without setting fruit. There are two garden plants which are frequently infected with the cucumber mosaic virus, lupins and delphiniums. The symptoms of the disease are much the same on both plants and consist of mottling and distortion of the leaves, stunting of the whole plant, and poor or malformed flowers. A delphinium plant infected with cucumber mosaic virus can be picked out at once from its healthy companions by its small size and stunted appearance.

Other garden plants which are commonly attacked by the cucumber mosaic virus are violas, zinnias, primulas, campanulas and aquilegias. Just recently, the chrysanthemum has been found in many parts of the country to be infected by a virus which appears to be related to cucumber mosaic virus although it will not attack the cucumber. The effect, however, on the chrysanthemum is serious and consists of mottling of the leaves and malformation of the flowers which renders them useless.

Tomato spotted wilt is a disease which in Great Britain is largely, but not entirely, a glasshouse problem. The virus is unusual in being transmitted by the thrips and not by aphids. It was first described in Australia in 1915, and about sixteen years later it appeared in this country and was identified at Cambridge in 1931 affecting a plant of *Solanum capsicastrum* from a Cardiff nursery (Smith, 1932).

Like the cucumber mosaic virus, the spotted wilt virus attacks a great variety of plants and this makes it rather difficult to eradicate. On tomatoes the symptoms are very characteristic and appear first as a number of reddish spots. These may run together, giving the leaves a metallic bronzing which is quite unmistakable and which is most pronounced in outdoor tomatoes. In certain plants this virus produces large numbers of concentric rings on the leaves, and this is another characteristic symptom to be on the watch for, especially in certain ornamental plants such as *Solanum capsicastrum*, dahlias and arum lilies. On gloxinias, the symptoms consist of large single rings with dark walls.

The dahlia is very susceptible to the virus of tomato spotted wilt, and there is a high percentage of infection amongst commercial stocks. In young affected plants the symptoms are usually of the ring-like character already mentioned, but older plants show a mottling of the leaves and a general stunting and unthriftiness. The virus is always present in the tubers of infected dahlia plants, and such tubers offer a ready means of dispersal of the virus about the country, and probably from country to country.

Other plants commonly infected with the spotted wilt virus are chrysanthemums, zinnias, primulas, *Tropaeolum* and many plants belonging to the Solanaceae.

We have thus far discussed briefly some of the effects of the cucumber mosaic and tomato spotted wilt viruses, and though we shall have occasion to discuss the former virus again in relation to another garden plant, it will be convenient at this juncture to consider a third virus. This virus is primarily the concern of the market gardener and smallholder but is also universally present in the ordinary flower and vegetable garden. The story of its first discovery is rather an interesting one and is intimately connected with the homely wallflower. For some time it had been noticed that the favourite blood-red wallflower was no longer true to type but carried flowers with a rather displeasing yellow fleck or stripe. There seemed at first no obvious reason for this colour change, and seeds from plants showing the yellow fleck in their flowers gave rise to plants with normal flowers when grown in the glasshouse. However, inoculation experiments using the tobacco as an indicator showed that the striping in the flowers was due to a virus. A leaf of a tobacco plant when inoculated with sap from wallflower petals with the yellow fleck develops spots on the leaf, which are foci of virus multiplication.

Further investigations connected this colour change in wallflowers with a serious state of degeneration in the broccoli and other brassicas, and it was found that both were due to an aphid-transmitted virus to which the name " cabbage black ringspot " was given because of the symptoms it causes in that plant. Since these early investigations it has been found that many other ornamental plants belonging to the cruciferae besides the wallflower are frequently infected with the same virus and undergo a similar colour " break " in the flowers. Examples of these are Stocks, *Arabis* and Sweet Rocket.

Lilies and tulips are two popular garden plants which are frequently infected with viruses, and since several viruses are concerned it will probably be easier to discuss these as they affect lilies and tulips rather than under the heading of individual viruses as has been the procedure hitherto. The virus diseases of these two plants are frequently composite in nature, particularly those affecting the lily, and this makes both their description and the control measures rather more difficult. Before discussing these composite diseases, where more than one virus is involved, it will be as well to deal with the disease caused by the cucumber mosaic virus to which reference has already been made.

In tulips the cucumber mosaic virus causes a mottling of the leaves which is produced by longitudinal grey streaks. These begin to develop about the time of flowering. A colour break is also present in the flower similar to the familiar colour break caused by tulip mosaic (Frontispiece) but differing slightly in that the edges of the streaks are less sharply defined. The outer perianth parts usually show a characteristic blemish and are shorter than normal.

In lilies this virus, by itself, seems to cause very slight mottling symptoms and in some species possibly no symptoms at all. It does, however, play a rather important part in the composite diseases above referred to.

The virus diseases of lilies in Great Britain have been very little investigated, but considerable work has been carried out on these diseases in the U.S.A. by Brierley and Smith (1944 a and b), and much of the following information is from their work. It cannot be said precisely, however, how far these results are applicable to lilies grown in England.

There seem to be three viruses commonly associated with lily diseases; these are cucumber mosaic virus, lily mottle virus and the so-called lily symptomless virus. The common disease in Easter lilies (*Lilium longiflorum*) is known as " necrotic fleck." In this disease severe leaf symptoms are caused, consisting of pale flecks usually parallel to the veins. These flecks dry out into brown necrotic spots. Affected lilies show dwarfing, curling of the leaves and distortion of the flowers, and tend to lose their leaves from below upwards after flowering.

The experimental production of this disease in lilies is rather interesting. It was found that inoculation of virus-free seedlings of Easter lily with cucumber mosaic virus did not produce the necrotic fleck disease, but similar inoculations of commercial Easter lilies did do so. This led the American workers to postulate the existence of a lily symptomless virus which, in the presence of cucumber mosaic virus, gives rise to the rather severe disease of necrotic fleck. From this it seems clear that commercial Easter lilies are usually infected with the lily symptomless virus but seedlings are not. Thus the addition of cucumber mosaic virus to the commercial Easter lilies gives rise to the composite disease of necrotic fleck but does not do so in seedlings since one of the components of the disease is missing.

The aphid, *Aphis gossypii*, is apparently able to transmit both components of necrotic fleck, but not the aphids *Macrosiphum solanifolii* and *Myzus persicae*. These two latter insects can, however, transmit the cucumber mosaic virus so that they could induce the disease in commercial Easter lilies by adding the second constituent virus to plants already infected with the symptomless virus.

The third lily virus which causes a mottling of the leaves and is known as the lily mottle or mosaic virus is common enough in lilies and occurs in company with the other two viruses. It is not, apparently, a necessary component of the necrotic fleck disease. The insect vectors are three species of aphid, *A. gossypii*, *M. persicae* and *M. solanifolii*.

An apparently new virus affecting lilies has recently been described. It was found infecting some lilies imported into this country from the U.S.A., and whilst the symptoms produced on the American hybrid lilies were mild enough, on the English lilies such as *Lilium tigrinum* and *L. regale* the effect was very severe. Affected plants of *L. tigrinum* developed necrosis and scorching of the leaves, the whole plant was stunted and no flowers were formed. Frequently the plant was killed. This virus is aphid-borne and is easily transmitted by the aphid *Myzus persicae* (Smith, 1950).

The lily mottle-mosaic virus is probably the same as, or related to, the tulip breaking virus, which we have not yet described. The outstanding symptom of this disease in tulips is, of course, the " break " or change in flower colour. This consists of a delicate variegation made up of streaks or pencillings of another colour which is sometimes very attractive (Frontispiece). In addition the leaves show a mosaic mottle, made up of longitudinal streaks. On the whole, the disease is not serious, though affected plants tend to be smaller and less thrifty than normal plants.

Another virus disease of tulips which has only recently been described and which threatens to become a serious menace to this plant, has an unusual and interesting history. To start at the beginning we must go back to 1935, when investigations at Cambridge revealed the existence of a virus which differed in its behaviour in many ways from that usual to plant viruses. A casual observation led to its discovery. It was noticed that the leaves of young tobacco plants growing in the glasshouse occasionally developed a lesion, a roundish spot of dead tissue, but only if the leaf happened to be in contact with the soil of the pot. When inoculations were made from this lesion to the leaves of other tobacco plants, French beans, etc., large numbers of lesions developed on these leaves showing that a virus was involved. It was observed, however, that no disease of the whole plant resulted, as is usual with viruses, but this virus remained confined to the inoculated leaf. In due course the infected leaf dried up and fell off, leaving the plant free of virus. Inoculation tests were then made of roots of tobacco and other plants which from their appearance seemed perfectly healthy, and it was discovered that in a considerable proportion of cases the virus was present in the roots, where it remained without causing any disease. Further

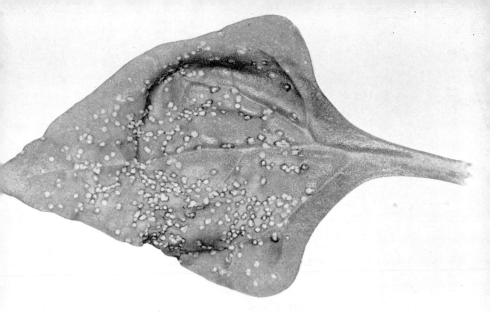

Plate Ia. Local lesions of tobacco necrosis virus on a leaf of New Zealand spinach

b. Local lesions on tobacco caused by tobacco ringspot virus

Plate II. Curious outgrowths or " enations " caused by the tomato black ring virus on cucumber

investigation showed that the virus was also present in the soil, where it could persist for long periods.

No insect vector has been discovered for this virus, and it is spread by being carried in the watering-can or in pieces of dried leaf-tissue to the soil whence it enters the roots by ruptured root hairs. Since the effect of this virus is to kill the cells (necrosis) without any mosaic or mottling disease, the name given to it was the *tobacco necrosis virus*. Up to a few years ago, therefore, this virus had never been found outside a glasshouse, and it had never been known to spread through an infected plant, causing a general or " systemic " disease (Smith and Bald, 1935).

The scene now changes to Holland, where for some years an unknown disease of field crops of French beans, called " stipple-streak," had been causing serious losses. Samples of this virus were obtained from Holland and found to be identical with, or closely related to, the tobacco necrosis virus in Cambridge. A small plot of French beans growing out-of-doors was infected with the Dutch virus in the expectation that it would spread through the plot. On the contrary, however, it behaved like the English virus and remained in the inoculated leaves without even spreading through one plant, to say nothing of other plants in the plot.

Now we come to the tulip. A year or two ago, a number of tulips imported from Holland showed a severe disease; the leaves were streaked and covered with dead patches whilst the flowers, if produced at all, were small and malformed. These plants were found to be infected with one or more of the tobacco necrosis viruses; the plural is used because it is known that there are several of these viruses biologically similar but serologically different.

It is now quite a common thing to find tulips infected with a tobacco necrosis virus and, as previously mentioned, the disease may become a serious trouble. Recently the virus has been found attacking *Primula obconica*; in one case it was present without visible symptoms, in the other the plant was killed by the virus.

We have here, then, a rather interesting state of affairs, but

what is the true explanation? Have we seen the development of
a new virus disease since the first description in 1935 of the
relatively non-pathogenic virus which was confined to the roots
of apparently healthy plants? And, if so, has this been achieved
by the appearance of different virus mutants which are capable
of becoming systemically distributed throughout the plant?

Just recently two apparently new viruses have appeared in
nasturtiums (*Tropaeolum* sp.). One of these was first found
infecting broad beans, on which it produced a kind of mottling
of dark green blisters. Later in the summer this virus was found
again, this time on nasturtiums, on which it was fairly widespread
in the Cambridge district. Affected plants were small and stunted
with a tendency towards a rosetted type of growth. The leaves
were crinkled, smaller than normal, and showed numerous
necrotic spots; some mosaic mottling of the leaves was also
present. The virus is aphid-transmitted, and experiments have
shown that both *Myzus persicae* and the black bean aphid, *Aphis
fabae*, can act as vectors. One interesting point about this virus
is the very characteristic type of symptoms produced on various
Solanaceous plants used as test plants for the virus. On *Nicotiana
glutinosa*, very conspicuous concentric rings develop, whilst on
Petunia sp. rings develop not only on the leaves but on the flowers
as well (Smith, 1950).

The second virus attacking *Tropaeolum* was discovered the
year after, in the same garden in plants arising from seed obtained
from the previous year's stock. This virus resembles the first in
some ways, but the disease produced in the nasturtiums is more
masked, the leaves being brightly and variously mottled with
less necrosis. The symptoms produced on test plants, such as
tobacco and *N. glutinosa*, are also different. Red flowers of
affected *Tropaeolum* plants show a pale " break," together with
a certain amount of distortion of the petals. This virus is also
aphid-transmitted.

Among other flowering plants frequently infected with
viruses are narcissi and sweet peas. The common mosaic disease
in narcissus used to be called " stripe " because of the longitudinal
markings on the leaves. These consist of light green or yellow

streaks which run parallel to the long axis of the leaf blade. Sometimes the streaks run the whole length of the leaf, but more often they are broken and may coalesce, forming isolated patches. In the foliage of some varieties, notably 'King Alfred,' dead patches of tissue may occur. Distortion of the foliage is another common symptom and the leaves may be spirally twisted. A white " break " also occurs in the flowers of some yellow varieties such as ' Golden Emperor,' ' Sir Watkin ' and ' King Alfred.'

The mode of spread of the virus in England is almost certainly by means of aphids. This has been shown to be the case in America, though no one in this country has identified the aphid concerned. Curiously enough, narcissi are very seldom seen infected with aphids, and the only species which seems capable of multiplying on the plant is *Macrosiphum solanifolii*, the common tulip aphid and vector of the tulip " break " virus.

The sweet pea is susceptible to a number of viruses, but under the ordinary garden conditions it is usually one particular virus which is concerned. This is the virus of common pea mosaic, and in addition to the sweet pea it affects the culinary pea, the broad bean and various clovers such as black medick (*Medicago lupulina*), crimson clover (*Trifolium incarnatum*) and red clover (*Trifolium pratense*).

On the sweet pea the main symptom is a pronounced " break " in coloured flowers. The leaves are mottled with a speckly mosaic of light and dark green. The virus is carried by the common pea aphid (*Macrosiphum pisi*), which feeds on a number of leguminous plants. This is rather unfortunate for the grower of both sweet and culinary peas because the life-cycle of this aphid is spent only on leguminous plants, most of which are susceptible to the pea mosaic virus. In consequence, when the aphid migrates to peas, after having spent the winter as an egg or hibernating female on clover, it frequently arrives already infected with the virus, which it has picked up from the perennial clover crop.

Another virus, also aphid-borne, which occasionally affects the sweet pea, produces a rather similar mottling of the leaves but differs from the foregoing in that small outgrowths or

" enations " develop on the under-surfaces of the leaves. Another difference is the absence of a colour " break " in the flowers.

Owing to the high price of smoking tobacco, many smokers have now taken to growing a small quantity of tobacco plants in their gardens, hoping by this means to be independent of imported supplies. Now, as it happens, the tobacco plant, for some reason, seems to be more susceptible to infection by viruses than most other plants, and indeed is used by virus workers as a test or " indicator " plant for suspected virus infection. We may, therefore, reasonably expect an increase in the number of viruses in gardens which contain a crop of tobacco. This plant when grown in a garden is usually infected with the cucumber mosaic virus. Other viruses which may be expected to infect tobacco are two potato viruses and, of course, the ever-present tobacco mosaic virus itself. This virus, as you may remember, was the first to be discovered and it has been studied more intensively perhaps than any other plant virus. This is chiefly because of certain properties such as stability, high concentration in the plant, its infectious nature and so forth. In addition to being the first virus to be discovered, it was also the first virus to be isolated in a more or less pure condition and we will discuss that further in another chapter. At the moment we are concerned with the part played by the tobacco mosaic virus in the garden.

The host range of this virus is fairly wide, but it is seldom found naturally infecting many garden plants though it may infect phlox on occasion. In America a strain of the tobacco mosaic virus is found fairly widespread in the common plantain (*Plantago major*). This weed apparently plays a considerable part in acting as a source of infection for tomatoes, in which this particular strain of virus causes an internal browning disease of the fruit.

In England, however, where the amount of tobacco grown is comparatively very small, such a contingency is unlikely to occur.

Various strains of the tobacco mosaic virus are, however, of great importance to growers of tomatoes both outside and under glass. These give rise to the different forms of tomato mosaic, aucuba, enation, streak, etc.

The common mottling type of tomato mosaic is extremely prevalent, much more so than it ought to be, and it is no unusual thing to find 70-80 per cent of the plants in a commercial glasshouse infected with this virus. The tomato mosaic virus is not insect-transmitted but is spread mechanically in infective sap from plant to plant on the hands and implements during the ordinary procedures of tending the plants. One or two infected plants are sufficient to contaminate by this means all the plants in a house containing several thousand, and once infection has become established in a glasshouse it is exceedingly difficult to eradicate as all the woodwork, implements, etc., become saturated with active virus and act as sources for further infections in following seasons.

References

Brierley, P., and Smith, Floyd F. (1944a). Studies on lily virus diseases: the necrotic fleck complex in *Lilium longiflorum*. *Phytopath, 34*: 529-55.

Brierley, P., and Smith, Floyd F. (1944b). Studies on lily virus diseases: the mottle group. *Phytopath, 34*: 718-46.

Smith, Kenneth M. (1932). Further experiments with a ringspot virus: its identification with spotted wilt of the tomato. *Ann. Appl. Biol. 19*: 305-30.

Smith, Kenneth M. (1950). Some new virus diseases of ornamental plants. *J. Roy. Hort. Soc. 75*: 350-53.

Smith, Kenneth M., and Bald, J. G. (1935). A description of a necrotic virus disease affecting tobacco and other plants. *Parasitology, 27*: 231-45.

CHAPTER 5

THE FARM

IN THE LAST chapter we discussed the virus diseases which affect the flowering plants and vegetables grown in the average English garden, and although we only dealt with some of the viruses, they were sufficiently varied to indicate the large number which are liable to attack garden plants. On the farm, however, if we except the virus diseases of livestock, the number of viruses involved is not large. This, of course, is partly due to the fact that the range and variety of crops on the English farm is small compared to the multiplicity of garden plants and partly to the absence, at present, of any viruses affecting the Gramineae in this country. This happy state of affairs may not last indefinitely, especially as a virus disease has recently been discovered in the cocksfoot (*Dactylis glomerata*). If we leave out of consideration, therefore, all the corn crops, we have to deal mainly with potatoes and sugar-beet and, to a lesser extent, the cruciferous crops.

Although the viruses affecting agricultural crops may be few in number, they are of very great economic importance and, in the case of potatoes, are estimated to reduce the crop by one million tons per annum.

Virus diseases of the potato have been a source of worry to the agricultural community since very early times. The so-called " potato curl," which seems to have made its first appearance in this country about 1770, is now known to have been a sort of general term for a number of viruses which are still under study at the present time. The literature on the potato viruses is rather confusing, and this confusion is emphasised by the many references to potato viruses under different letters of the alphabet. We can, however, at the risk of some over-simplification, clarify the situation by putting the potato viruses of this country into three groups.

The first group, if such a term is permissible, contains only one virus, that of potato leaf-roll and any strains that it may have; the second contains the large and important series of viruses of which virus X is the type strain of virus, and also includes potato viruses B and D. Group 3 contains potato virus Y and its various strains. In other words, with the exception of potato leaf-roll and a few relatively unimportant viruses, the potato viruses in England may be regarded as mainly of the two types, viruses X and Y and their strains.

POTATO VIRUS X

The disease caused by virus X in potatoes is not severe and as a rule consists of a mild mottling of the leaves, though the symptoms may increase somewhat in intensity with the more virulent strains of the virus. That a virus causing such a mild disease should be economically so important may appear somewhat surprising, but the main importance of the virus lies in its universal distribution, and the consequent regular reduction in the yield of the world's potato crop.

Because of its great importance much attention has been paid to the study of this virus and in consequence a good deal is known about it. In describing some of the more interesting facts about potato virus X, we can start with the origin of its rather peculiar name, which was given to it by one of us in 1931. Previous to this, the virus had been known in the U.S.A. by the even more peculiar and contradictory name of the " healthy potato virus." This name arose partly from the fact that, apart from seedlings, not a single potato plant in America was free from the virus and partly because an American worker, James Johnson, had shown in 1925 that inoculations from apparently healthy potatoes to tobacco produced in that plant either a mottling or ringspot disease. Alternative names for the virus thus came to be " potato mottle " or " potato ringspot." We see from this experiment of Johnson's, therefore, that the virus may be entirely symptomless in some potato varieties (Johnson, 1925).

In carrying out transmission experiments at Cambridge from virus-diseased potatoes it was discovered that the type of disease produced in the experimentally inoculated plants differed with the *method* of virus transmission used. To digress for a moment, it should be explained that in testing a plant for the presence of a virus, it is frequently necessary to use some other kind of plant to serve as an indicator. Such plants usually react more quickly or more characteristically to a given virus than the original host plant. In the experiments here described the test plant used was the tobacco, which Johnson used earlier, and transmissions were made to tobacco plants from the same diseased potato plants by two methods, i.e. by inoculation and by means of a species of aphid (*Myzus persicae*). It was found that the mechanical method of sap inoculation produced in the tobacco plant a severe disease characterised by patches of dead cells (necrosis) and stunting of the whole plant. Transmission by means of the aphid, however, from the same potato plant to tobacco gave rise to quite a different disease, with very mild symptoms consisting of a characteristic dark banding of the veins. This production of two different diseases in the indicator plant by different methods of transmission suggested that more than one virus was concerned in the disease and that they differed in their method of transmission. In other words, what was happening was that the aphid was picking out one virus which gave rise to the vein-banding disease on tobacco whilst mechanical transmission by means of sap passed over both viruses. In order to obtain the second virus in pure culture, it was necessary to eliminate the aphid-transmitted virus, and this was done by means of what may be called a " filter plant." The plant used was *Datura stramonium*, the thorn apple, which was found to be immune to the aphid-transmitted virus; passage of the complex to this plant by inoculation and thence to tobacco therefore filtered out this virus and gave in tobacco a pure culture of the second virus. The two viruses were given the names of Potato Viruses X and

Y, X being the virus which is not aphid-transmitted, and Y the aphid-transmitted virus, causing the vein-banding disease in tobacco. It is by these letters that the two chief potato viruses are now generally known (Smith, 1931).

We have said that potato virus X is practically world-wide in its distribution, and it is probably present wherever the potato plant is grown on a large scale. It has long been thought that the virus had been associated with the potato for an indefinite time, probably since it was first cultivated in Europe. Van der Plank (1949), however, suggests that the virus has become destructive only in this century and has collected interesting evidence to support his suggestion, some of which is briefly given here. In 1833 missionaries going to Basutoland took with them, among other necessaries, a number of seed potatoes. These have been grown by the natives ever since, but only in small patches among maize, etc., since the potato is not a staple food. Now after over a century several hundred of these " native " potatoes have been tested and found free from virus X. Only when they have been grown beside modern varieties in experimental plots or kitchen gardens have they been found infected.

Further evidence comes from Tristan da Cunha, about midway between the Cape and South America. In 1816 a garrison from the Cape landed there and apparently took potatoes with them. At all events potatoes were abundant and seemed to have formed the chief food of the islanders. Two varieties of potato were apparently grown, one pink-skinned and the other white-skinned. The white-skinned variety resembles the old types with numerous deep eyes and has the general appearance of the potatoes described in Europe in the first half of the nineteenth century. Dr. Van der Plank tested a fairly large sample of these potatoes and found them still free of virus X in spite of the fact that, unlike conditions in Basutoland, the potatoes had been grown in a concentrated area under intensive conditions which would have encouraged the spread of virus X if it had been present. Probably now the virus has entered Tristan da Cunha with stocks of potatoes imported during the last war, and it must be only a matter of time before the original stocks become infected.

Recently some more evidence on the same lines is available from Kenya. The potato variety ' Northern Star ' was introduced into Britain in 1900, where it had a brief boom and then faded out. However, some time fairly early after its introduction it was sent to Kenya, where the natives grew it under the names Kinongo and Keiai. As in the case of the varieties of Basutoland and Tristan da Cunha, " Northern Star " in Kenya is a relic of the past but, as Van der Plank points out, the date of its introduction to Kenya can be more accurately determined. Numbers of these potatoes from native shambas have been tested recently and found still free of virus X.

Van der Plank concludes from his study of the history of potato virus X that we should take warning of the danger of modern cultural practices. He says: " Losses from virus X, conservatively put at 800,000,000 bushels a year for the world over, are both an indictment of the organisation of the seed industry and a warning against the danger of abandoning varietal abundance and novelty in crops which are propagated by vegetative means."

We have shown in Chapter 3 the close relationship of viruses with insects and how many plant viruses are disseminated by insect vectors. In our discussion, however, in this chapter of the analysis of the X and Y virus complex, it was made clear that potato virus X was not insect- or at all events not aphid-transmitted. Since then, many experiments with other types of insects have failed to find a vector for this virus. Yet it is an ubiquitous virus, world-wide in its distribution. How, then, does it spread in the field? This remained a secret for many years until experiments in Ireland with potatoes and in this country with tobacco showed that a healthy plant could be infected by contact with a diseased one. The bruising of the leaves of potato plants by knocking against each other in the rows is sufficient for the virus to be passed over. It has been shown recently at Rothamsted that spread of the virus can also take place between plants whose only contact is below ground (Roberts, 1948).

Such infection, of course, could only occur with a virus which is in high concentration in the sap and is also mechanically transmissible. So far as we know, this is the only method by which potato virus X is spread in nature; if there is an insect vector it has not yet been identified.

Since it has been mentioned more than once that virus X produces very little obvious disease and may cause no symptoms at all, the reader may wonder why the virus is of so much importance. However, experiments at various centres have shown that the presence of virus X in a potato crop, even if it is a symptomless strain, may reduce the crop by as much as ten per cent, besides which, plants infected with the virus react much more severely when other viruses like Y or A get into them.

The seed certification scheme has helped greatly to check the spread of the aphid-transmitted potato viruses, leaf-roll and virus Y, and this has served to throw virus X into greater prominence. The virulent strains of this virus have also been largely eliminated by careful inspections of seed crops, but the more insidious latent or symptomless forms cannot be eradicated by visual inspection. The consequence of this has been that symptomless strains of the X virus occur commonly in some of the best Scotch seed of certain potato varieties.

It may be of interest here to describe briefly how the presence of a latent virus X in a potato may be confirmed. By means of certain tests, it is possible to check over a stock of seed potatoes in the winter time before the crop is sown, to find out the infected tubers, and to gain an idea of the amount of virus present. Some of the more progressive seed potato growers are using these methods to build up a nucleus stock of virus-free potatoes which can be propagated under conditions of isolation from virus infection.

We have already seen one method of testing for the presence of virus X in the description of the analysis of the X and Y virus complex. This is the use of test, or indicator, plants which react more clearly, quickly, and unmistakably to infection than the potato plant itself. In the experiment described, tobacco seedlings were employed, and these are still much in use for this purpose.

Other indicator plants are the thorn apple, *Datura stramonium*, and more recently, a plant belonging to the Amarantaceae, *Gomphrena globosa*, the globe amaranth. This plant responds to infection even with the symptomless strains of virus X with the formation, on the inoculated leaves, of clear round spots of a dark red colour. These are known as " local lesions "; they develop a few days after inoculation and cannot possibly be overlooked.

For the winter testing of dormant potato tubers for the presence of virus X a heated glasshouse is necessary for raising the indicator plants. It is also necessary for forcing " eyes " of the potato tubers if winter testing is employed. An " eye " is removed from the tuber by means of a cork-borer and grown in sterilised sand or soil in the glasshouse. When a shoot a few inches long has been obtained, this is ground up in a mortar and inoculated to the test plant. Another and quicker, if slightly less reliable method, consists in rubbing the tuber on a strip of coarse sandpaper, so as to excoriate the skin, and then rubbing the abraded portion on to the leaf of the test plant. This avoids having to grow an " eye " in sterilised soil.

Another method which in recent times has been much developed for the testing for viruses is by means of the serological reactions. Most plant viruses, provided they are present in the sap of the host plant in sufficient quantity, are good antigens. This means that if they are injected into the bloodstream of a suitable animal, such as the rabbit, antibodies are produced. These antibodies (antiserum) react in an observable way when mixed with the original virus (antigen) and closely related viruses, but not with unrelated viruses. This gives a rapid method of testing for the presence of virus X in the sap of a potato plant without the necessity of waiting for the development of symptoms in the test plant, which may take two or three weeks (Markham, Matthews and Smith, 1948).

POTATO VIRUS Y

The disease of severe mosaic so-called, induced in potato,

plants by virus Y is, as its name implies, more injurious to the plant than the leaf-mottling disease due to virus X. An alternative name for the disease is " leaf-drop streak " because the leaves shrivel and die but remain hanging attached to the plant while a streak of dead tissue frequently runs longitudinally down the stem. The general effect of the disease is superficially similar in appearance to an attack of " blight " (*Phytophthora infestans*).

The properties and general behaviour of virus Y are very different from virus X and, as we have already seen, it is by taking advantage of this fact that the two can be separated. Although virus Y can be transmitted mechanically easily enough, in nature it is entirely dependent upon aphids for its transfer from plant to plant. The chief vector is the small peach and potato aphid, *Myzus persicae*, but other potato aphids also act as subsidiary vectors.

Virus Y is of the type of insect-transmitted viruses known as " non-persistent," which roughly means that they can be picked up by the aphid from an infected plant after it has fed for a few minutes. Such viruses differ from " persistent " viruses, of which potato leaf-roll is an example, in being rapidly lost by the insect vector (see Chap. 3, p. 17). After feeding for a short time on a plant the aphid is no longer infective.

It is seldom necessary to test a potato plant for the presence of virus Y because the symptoms produced by it are fairly characteristic. Nevertheless, if it is desired to make such a test, there are certain plants which can be used for this purpose. One is the tobacco plant, which reacts to infection with virus Y by the development of the so-called " clearing of the veins " whereby the veins of the youngest leaves stand out from the surrounding tissue. The other is the " Duke of Argyll's tea plant " (*Lycium* sp.), which reacts to inoculation with virus Y by the formation of round discrete spots similar to those produced by virus X on the leaves of the globe amaranth.

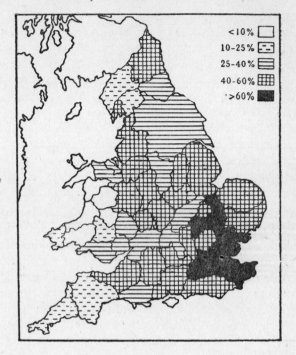

FIG. I

Proportion of Scotch and Irish seed potatoes planted in counties
of England and Wales, 1942. (*Samuel, Ann. appl. Biol., 1943*)

POTATO LEAF-ROLL

In this disease, as the name implies, the leaves show a greater
or less amount of rolling, which varies with the variety of potato
affected.   In all varieties, however, there is a tendency of the
leaves to roll upwards and inwards, accompanied by a harshness
and toughening of the texture.   This leathery texture of the
leaves is due to accumulation of starch.   The effect of leaf-roll
on the yield is very serious, and the reduction may be as much
as ninety per cent with some varieties.   Unlike potato viruses
X and Y, the leaf-roll virus is not transmissible by sap-inoculation.

Apart from grafting, which is an almost universal method of virus transmission, it can only be transmitted by means of the aphid vector, which, again, is mainly the potato and peach aphid, *Myzus persicae*. One or two other species of aphid can also act as subsidiary vectors of the virus, but other kinds of insect cannot do so.

It may perhaps be worth while to point out how profoundly the potato virus diseases, which we have briefly discussed, affect the agricultural community in England. Each year nearly 400,000 tons of seed potatoes are imported into England, and within the space of two or three years practically all this seed is discarded as unsuitable for further propagation because it has become infected with virus diseases. Samuel (1943) has prepared a map showing the extent to which this import of fresh potato " seed " is practised in different parts of England, and this map is reproduced in Fig. 1. It will be seen that in the counties shown black, a large number of growers buy new seed each year from Scotland or Ireland. The black area includes East Anglia, where deterioration of potatoes from virus infections is most rapid and complete. In counties cross-hatched the seed may be said to last on the average for two years; in those with horizontal lines about three years; in those with broken lines about five or six years; and in certain counties in Wales, shown in white, about ten years. Actually some parts of Wales are sufficiently isolated and are otherwise suitable for propagating seed potatoes, and a certain amount of good seed potatoes are actually raised there.

Sugar-beet, Mangold and Turnip Viruses

Next in importance on the farm to the viruses affecting potatoes are those which attack the sugar-beet and mangold crops. Luckily we are only concerned here with two viruses, although they are serious enough. The diseases they cause are known as sugar-beet *mosaic* and *virus yellows*, the latter being the more important.

The symptoms of the two diseases are briefly as follows: in

mosaic, the first sign of infection is a clearing and yellowing of the veins of the young central leaves. This is followed by the development of yellow or light green flecks or spots on the other leaves; these increase in size and the middle leaves of the plant show a fairly characteristic yellow and green mottling. The outer and older leaves usually show no symptoms. In *virus yellows*, the situation is reversed, there is no pronounced yellowing of the veins of the central leaves, indeed the centre of the plant remains normal in appearance whilst the outer or middle leaves become yellow, thickened and brittle. The yellowing usually begins at the tips and upper margins of the leaves and spreads downwards between the veins, giving a bright orange-yellow colour to the leaves, often with red or russet-brown patches. Infected leaves are also thickened and brittle, with a tendency to rustle, crackle, and splinter (Hull and Watson, 1945).

The natural means of transfer of these two viruses in the field is the same, by the agency of two species of aphid, the ubiquitous *Myzus persicae* and the black bean aphid, or " dolphin " (*Aphis fabae*).

Both viruses are mechanically transmissible by sap-inoculation, but the mosaic virus is much more easily transmitted by this means than is the yellows virus. Indeed it has only recently been shown that virus yellows can be transmitted in this way. It is necessary to use an abrasive such as fine carborundum powder during inoculation, which increases the number of entry points of the virus into the leaf. Even so, only a proportion, about ten per cent, of plants inoculated with yellows become fully infected. The others develop local lesions on the inoculated leaves without further spread of the virus.

In any case, the development of the full disease is retarded as compared with plants infected by means of the aphid, and this may be due to the fact that the insect delivers the virus directly into the phloem, whence it is carried rapidly to other parts of the plant.

The importance of these two viruses, and especially the yellows virus, to the grower lies in the reduction of the sugar yield, and this in turn is governed largely by the date of infection.

Plate III. Tumours on white sweet clover, caused by the wound tumour virus: note the tumour which has developed at the site of an injury by the edge of the pot (*after Black*)

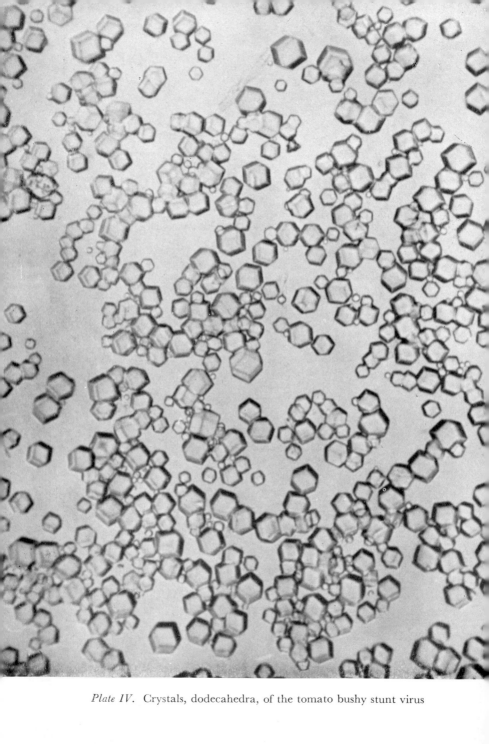

Plate IV. Crystals, dodecahedra, of the tomato bushy stunt virus

Thus, crops infected in June may have the sugar content reduced by half, whilst those infected in August and September show a very small reduction.

Since sugar-beet crops are started from seed, and since few viruses are seed-transmitted, it is easy enough to start with a virus-free crop. This, as we have already seen, is not the case with potatoes, where the virus may be, and usually is, present in the " seed " tuber. The trouble with the sugar-beet is to prevent the arrival of the virus in the crop. There are various sources of infection such as mangold clamps, volunteer beets or mangolds, and the varieties of beet such as seakale and spinach beet. One of the most important sources of virus, however, is the seed crop, which usually has a high percentage of infection with both viruses. The " stecklings," which have been sown in the summer, become heavily infected in the autumn. These stecklings are kept over the winter to become the seed crop the following year, and since it is often the practice to grow root and seed crop close together, a rich source of virus is always at hand. An obvious step, therefore, is to keep the root crop and the seed beet crop as far apart as is practicable.

We come now to the viruses affecting the turnip, the last of the farm crops to be dealt with. There are two viruses to be considered and one of them is unusual in several ways. These two are known as the cauliflower mosaic and turnip yellow mosaic viruses respectively.

Of these two viruses, the more important from the farmer's point of view, though the less interesting scientifically, is the cauliflower mosaic virus. A turnip plant infected with this virus is so severely diseased as to be useless, even if it is not killed. The insect vector is the aphid *Myzus persicae* and one or two other species which infest cruciferous crops. The virus is similar to the cabbage black ringspot virus which, as we saw in the last chapter, is frequently found infecting wallflowers (*Cheiranthus*), causing a colour " break " (Frontispiece). Indeed the two viruses often occur together in brassicas and other Cruciferae and are transmitted together by the same aphid.

In turnips the first sign of infection is a mottling and crinkling of the leaves; as the disease progresses, the crinkling becomes more severe and the growing point is rosetted in a characteristic way. In the last stages of the disease the yellow crinkled leaves lie flat on the ground; secondary rotting often sets in and the plant is killed. In certain parts of the country, particularly in East Anglia, this disease is very prevalent and is a limiting factor in the growing of turnips.

Turnip yellow mosaic (Frontispiece), whilst having a less severe effect on the plant, is nevertheless a potentially important disease because of the ubiquity of its insect vector.

The first sign of infection is a pronounced yellowing or " clearing " of the veins of the youngest leaves. This is followed by the appearance of yellow flecks and patches on the older leaves which finally merge, producing an extremely bright yellow mosaic. This mosaic is unusually pronounced and is more suggestive of a variegation than of a disease.

As we have already mentioned, the virus causing turnip yellow mosaic is of considerable scientific interest, being unusual in several ways. It is the only virus, so far described in this country, which is transmitted by an insect with biting mouth parts instead of the more usual sap-sucking aphids. Various kinds of biting insects can be induced, under experimental conditions, to transmit the virus, but, under natural conditions, the insect vector is one or more species of the turnip flea beetle, *Phyllotreta* spp. The turnip flea beetles constitute one of the worst pests with which the British farmer has to deal, and it is because of their great numbers and wide distribution that this virus becomes a potential menace. There is, however, one fact in connection with the turnip yellow mosaic virus which may help to prevent its becoming widespread, and that relates to the question of over-wintering. We have seen how one of the other viruses which attack brassicas, such as the cabbage black ringspot virus, by reason of its wide host range, can easily over-winter in biennial and perennial plants like wallflowers and *Arabis*. The host range of the turnip yellow mosaic virus, however, is more restricted and it does not appear capable of infecting any of the ornamental plants belonging to the Cruciferae. It can, however, infect kale and also kohlrabi and broccoli, but apparently only with difficulty, and the winter may be passed in some such host as this. It is, of course, a well-known fact that the flea beetles, the vectors of the virus, hibernate as adult beetles, but there is no evidence that virus-carrying beetles can retain their infectivity over the winter months (Markham and Smith, 1949).

References

HULL, R., and WATSON, M. A. (1945). Virus yellows of sugar-beet. *Agriculture, 52*: 66-70.

JOHNSON, J. (1925). Transmission of viruses from apparently healthy potatoes. *Bull. Wis. Agric. Exp. Sta. 63*: 12-00.

MARKHAM, R., MATTHEWS, R. E. F., and SMITH, KENNETH M. (1948). Testing potato stocks for virus X. *Farming, 2*: 40-46.

MARKHAM, R., and SMITH, KENNETH M. (1949). Studies on the virus of turnip yellow mosaic. *Parasitology, 39*: 330-42.

ROBERTS, F. M. (1948). Experiments on the spread of potato virus X between plants in contact. *Ann. Appl. Biol. 35*: 266-78.

SAMUEL, G. (1943). Potato virus diseases: introduction. *Ann. Appl. Biol. 30*: 80-82.

SMITH, KENNETH M. (1931). On the composite nature of certain potato virus diseases of the mosaic group as revealed by the use of plant indicators and selective methods of transmission. *Proc. Roy. Soc. (B.) 109*: 251-67.

VAN DER PLANK, J. C. (1949). Some suggestions on the history of potato virus X. *Journ. Linn. Soc. Bot. 53*: 251-62.

CHAPTER 6

SOME EVERYDAY VIRUS DISEASES

IN THIS CHAPTER we give a short account of some of the more common virus diseases affecting animals. Of those attacking man, two are intimately associated with childhood, the others, such as influenza and the common cold, are perennially with us.

Mumps was one of the first diseases to be recognised as a separate and distinct entity. This was in the fifth century B.C., and its most common symptoms and manifestations were clearly recorded by Hippocrates, who described it as a mild epidemic sickness characterised by non-suppurative swellings near the ears. Now, two thousand years later, we have not much to add to his description.

For many years, the cause of mumps was unknown, and it was only as recently as 1934 that two workers, Johnson and Goodpasture, proved it to be due to a virus. Like so many other virus diseases, infection appears to be by droplet spread, that is by the secretions from the mouth and nose. Man himself is the only reservoir of the virus, and fairly close contact seems to be necessary for infection to take place. Mumps is an endemic disease in urban populations, that is to say it never completely dies out, but flares up at intervals, usually during winter and early spring. At longer intervals of seven or eight years, severe epidemics may occur. The disease is most common in childhood, but adolescents and young adults are also susceptible.

So far as we know, the monkey is the only other animal susceptible to mumps, but the virus will grow on the chorio-allantoic membrane of the developing hen's egg. Both the monkey and the egg have played their part in experiments on the control of mumps, and there seem to be three possible lines of approach to the problem. Some success has been achieved in immunising man against the disease by means of emulsions of formalin-treated virus from the parotid glands of monkeys. Secondly, virus which has been grown in the hen's egg and inactivated by means of ether or ultra-violet light has been shown to protect monkeys against the disease; it has not been tried on man. The third method is to use virus which has been repeatedly passed through a series of eggs. This treatment attenuates the virus and makes it less virulent. Such attenuated virus seems to render monkeys solidly immune to re-infection.

Not very much appears to be known about the mumps virus itself. It has been photographed on the electron microscope and the size is about 200 mμ. As viruses go, this is very large when compared to plant viruses of 20 to 30 mμ (see Chap. 10, p. 102).

Measles was first recognised as an independent disease in the seventeenth century by the English physician Sydenham. It is a more severe and more infectious virus disease than the foregoing. It is extremely prevalent and the great majority of adults in civilised lands have suffered from measles. This fact is of importance as we shall see in discussing control measures against the disease. Butler, quoted by van Rooyen and Rhodes, investigated the measles history of 14,000 persons and found that 78 per cent at all ages had been attacked. Analysed, these figures showed that up to four years, 8·5 per cent had been affected, whilst over 15 years some 97·3 per cent had suffered from measles. Similarly, Collins found that 90 to 95 per cent of American students had been attacked.

In England, the greatest incidence of the disease is between November and March. This is shown by the mortality figures during the six years 1940-45 in London, which varied from 6·4 per thousand cases during the winter months to less than one per thousand during the summer.

A good instance of the extremely infectious nature of measles is the case of the " long window " quoted by Meenan. A boy, ill in bed, infected his aunt, who had never seen him during her stay in the house, and had in fact left the house on the morning after he had been sent to bed. On investigation it was found that one long window served two rooms on different floors, in such a way that one room had a direct connection with the other, because at the window there was a gap in the flooring. The patient was in the upstairs room and his aunt sat at meals directly below the gap. Twelve days later she developed measles.

Great epidemics of measles have occurred from time to time in all inhabited parts of the world, such, for example, as the " black measles " of the eighteenth century in London. Where there is " virgin soil," i.e. large populations which for some reason or other have avoided infection, the virus spreads with terrifying speed; an example of this is the epidemic in the Faroe Islands in 1846. Sometimes the virus is accompanied by secondary bacterial invaders as in the U.S. Army camps during the first world war.

In the Faroe Islands there was an epidemic of measles in 1781, but it was not until 1846 that the severe epidemic occurred. Within six months, 6,000 out of the 7,782 inhabitants had become infected. Those old persons who had had measles in 1781 were still immune, whereas their contemporaries who had escaped at that time now contracted it.

Nothing is known about the size and shape of the measles virus, but it can remain infectious outside the body at room temperature for more than 24 hours. The virus can also, like that of mumps, be propagated in the hen's egg, but this, when inoculated into man, does not regularly induce a very high resistance. Much the most hopeful line of treatment lies in the use of *gamma globulin*. From studies on the composition of human blood it has been discovered that the fluid component consists mainly of five proteins; albumin, fibrinogen, alpha globulin, beta globulin, and gamma globulin. This last-named is the fraction containing the highest proportion of antibodies and represents a 25-fold increase in antibody concentration over the original plasma. During the late war, large stocks of human blood were accumulated for blood transfusion, and efforts were made to find a use for those fractions of the blood not needed for transfusion purposes. Now, we have already stated that a very large proportion of adult human beings have had measles in their youth, so it was natural to find that the gamma globulin fraction of the processed human blood was rich in antibodies to measles.

Experiments carried out in the U.S.A. showed that if 1/10 ml. of the gamma globulin was injected per pound of body weight, the individuals were completely protected. The amount to be given and the time of administration depends on whether a complete but transitory protection against infection is desired, or an attenuation of the disease. It should, perhaps, be emphasised that where there is complete prevention of the disease, there is no subsequent protection, but modification to a mild attack confers long, if not life-long, immunity. So far no very convincing results have been obtained in the use of gamma globulin once the disease has started in the patient.

No account of everyday virus diseases would omit the virus, or viruses, of influenza. This disease has been known for centuries, but it was only shown to be due to a virus comparatively recently. The story really began with the work of an American, Shope, in 1931, who was studying a disease of pigs, swine influenza. Incidentally, swine influenza is thought to be a relic of the great influenza pandemic of 1918-19, of which we shall say more later on, which became adapted to pigs and has persisted in them ever since. Then in 1933, three English workers, Smith, Andrewes and Laidlaw, working in London, managed to infect ferrets which showed an influenza-like disease and developed neutralising antibodies. At the same time, they transmitted Shope's pig influenza virus to ferrets also and produced a similar disease to that caused by the human virus: both these viruses were later transferred to mice. In spite of these discoveries, influenza diseases occurred both in Britain and the U.S.A. which did not fit into the general picture. It was then shown by Francis, and also by Magill independently, in America, that there existed a second influenza virus which differed in several characteristics from the first one. These two influenza viruses are now known as viruses A and B. If the study of plant viruses provides any analogy, more letters of the alphabet will probably be needed in the future.

When a disease is epidemic over a whole country or over the whole world, it is known as a pandemic, and such pandemics of influenza have occurred at intervals since about the beginning of the twelfth century. The most recent and the greatest of all occurred after the first world war in the years 1918-19. On this occasion, about half the population of the world was attacked, and it is estimated that the total deaths amounted to over twenty million people. In the U.S.A. 550,000 deaths occurred and in Britain 220,000.

Since that time there have been several epidemics of influenza. In Great Britain, for example, there were epidemics of virus A in 1933, 1937 and 1943, whilst infections due to virus B occurred in 1939, 1943 and 1946.

Much intensive study has been carried out on the influenza viruses and quite a lot is known about them. They have been extensively studied with the electron microscope (see Plate XII, p. 117) and there is evidence that the virus may exist in more than one form. The usual appearance of the virus particle is rounded, ovoid, or slightly bean-shaped and measures about 80-100 mμ in diameter, but longer thread-like particles are also frequently present, some of which are seen in Plate XII. The exact significance of these long forms is not known, but it has been suggested that they may be stages in a multiplication cycle. There is some evidence that the particles of virus B are somewhat larger than those of virus A. The infectivity of virus A is destroyed by heating at 56° C. for about 20-30 minutes. If it is allowed to dry in air it may remain infective for several days, and this is important as we shall see later.

Some interesting experiments have been carried out to test the survival of influenza virus when sprayed into the air. It was found that in a small room the virus could be recovered after 30 minutes, but in an unusually dry atmosphere the virus might persist for 24 hours. The presence of infective virus in the atmosphere was determined by the use of mice; these little animals are susceptible to the virus and are readily infected by inhalation.

The virus can also remain active on the human skin for periods of 10-45 minutes.

Some of these properties of the virus are of importance in determining the methods of spread of influenza. The most common method of infection is undoubtedly by droplets from the nose and mouth of infected persons which are inhaled by others. However, since the virus will withstand a moderate amount of drying, infection may also take place by means of infected dust, by dried particles shaken out of blankets and possibly on eating and drinking utensils if insufficiently washed.

We have mentioned that in the first experiments to prove that influenza is caused by a virus, ferrets were used, and it is interesting to find that one of the workers was himself infected with influenza through the sneezing of an infected ferret. The virus isolated from this worker was found to be similar to the virus which had been passed through 195 ferrets and not to fresh virus. It seems, therefore, that, even after passage of so many ferrets, the virus still retained its infectivity for man.

A great deal of investigation has been carried out on vaccination against influenza. One of the great difficulties lies in the fact that there are the two different types of virus, A and B, and many strains of these two type viruses, so that any vaccine must contain strains of these two types. Most vaccines are prepared from virus grown in the chick embryo and then rendered inactive by the use of formalin and sometimes by ultra-violet light. In America, considerable success seems to have been achieved on occasion by the use of vaccines during influenza epidemics. The success, however, seems to depend on whether there is a close relationship between the strains of virus used in the vaccine and that causing the epidemic. If there is no close relationship, the vaccine will probably fail to evoke an effective immunity. However, there is still hope that an efficient vaccine will one day be prepared and in the meantime work towards this end is being promoted by the World Influenza Centre and by local health authorities.

There are, of course, other measures which help to reduce the risk of infection. A transparent mask made of cellulose acetate was introduced during the second world war, but here the psychological factor intervened and it was difficult to persuade persons to wear the mask continuously. The homely advice to sneeze or cough into a handkerchief still has much to recommend it. Some advantage may also be obtained by treatment of the air in crowded places by means of ultra-violet light irradiation or by the use of antiseptic mists or aerosols.

So far, no antibiotic, such as penicillin or aureomycin, has been found to be effective against the influenza viruses.

Before we conclude this brief account of the influenza viruses, it may be of interest to record a new tool which has recently been devised for charting the volume and direction of waves of sickness such as influenza. This tool is the statistics of claims on the national insurance fund for payments during illness, and its use for mapping influenza epidemics has recently been described in an interesting article in *The Times*. Local insurance offices notify any sudden or heavy increase in claims to the local health authorities and also to the Ministry of National Insurance. The Ministry receives these notifications when the claims in the local offices increase to two, three, or even five times the usual rate, and such danger signals only occur during influenza outbreaks. These abnormal numbers of claims provide epidemiologists with a useful check on the course of the epidemic and were first used during the outbreak of 1950-51. This seems to have begun in three port areas; Falmouth-Truro, Tyneside and Aberdeen. A second severer and apparently independent outbreak soon followed in Merseyside. From these centres the disease swept southwards throughout Britain in about three weeks. It is thought that one strain of virus came from Scandinavia through ports on the east coast of Britain while another more virulent strain came from the Mediterranean area through Liverpool. Similar data are being collected concerning the 1953 outbreak, which like that of 1951 seems to have been largely of the more severe A-type virus.

The common cold is a condition which occurs more frequently than all the other ailments of man combined and is responsible for an enormous annual loss in time and money. In the U.S.A.

the average infection works out at 2·5 attacks per person per annum. In spite of a good deal of research work, not very much progress has been made in our knowledge of the disease and its cause. It is fairly certain that a virus is the causal agent and chimpanzees have been infected with material which has been passed through bacteria-proof filters. On one or two occasions claims have been made that the virus has been cultivated in special chick embryo tissue but this has not been repeated lately. However, what is wanted is some small experimental animal such as the ferret which would be susceptible to the virus. At the moment the only susceptible animals known are the chimpanzee and man himself.

Little is known about the actual virus, but data obtained at the Common Cold Research Unit at Salisbury suggest that it is as small as or smaller than the virus of influenza. The virus is spread by droplet infection and also probably in dried secretions as dust shaken out of handkerchiefs, etc. There appears to be no effective treatment of the disease, other than retirement to bed, which benefits the patient and restricts the spread of infection. There are no control measures at present, and vaccines prepared from bacterial organisms from the nose and throat have not been shown, under controlled conditions, to decrease susceptibility to infection.

At fairly regular intervals a few cases of psittacosis, or parrot fever, as it is sometimes called, occur in man, and these are usually followed, and rightly so, by an embargo on the importation of parrots. Indeed several cases of the disease were reported in London at the end of 1952, when the manager of a pet shop in a large departmental store caught the infection and died.

The disease was first described by Ritter in the year 1880, when a household in Switzerland became infected, three out of the seven cases proving fatal. The owner of the house kept a number of parrots and there was an epidemic among these birds prior to the human infections. Since then, there have been many outbreaks over most of the Continent of Europe, some of them serious. In 1930 there was a pandemic of the disease which involved twelve countries, including Britain. After that, importation of parrots, except under licence, was forbidden, and this embargo, which had been lifted, has now been reimposed after the latest outbreak in 1952.

The virus occurs in a large number of birds, not all of them belonging to the parrot family. At least 31 species of the parrot family act as spontaneous hosts to the psittacosis virus. In addition Java ricebirds, canaries, finches, sparrows, domestic fowls, ducks, pigeons, doves, fulmars and American herring gulls are all susceptible. It seems probable also that a large number of London's pigeons are infected with a latent form of the virus.

Whilst the disease caused in parrots may be severe or fatal, there is no doubt that the virus is also carried in a latent condition by some birds, and these birds are a grave source of danger. Infection to man, causing a pneumonia-like disease, can be brought about in a number of different ways, by handling parrots or even by being bitten by them. The droppings, both of diseased birds and carriers, are infectious and so is the dust of infected droppings if inhaled. Bedson recalls how the disease attacks only women in the Faroe Islands because they are employed in the stripping and salting-down of young fulmars for winter food. Psittacosis also occurs quite commonly as an occupational disease of bird fanciers.

Quite a lot is known about the virus of psittacosis; it is very large, about 450 mμ in diameter, and is grouped with the Rickettsiae, which come between the small viruses and the bacteria in size. Although it is classed with the Rickettsiae, this seems at present unjustified because these agents, of which typhus is characteristic, are all associated with insects or other arthropods, and there is at present no evidence of this with psittacosis.

The obvious method to avoid psittacosis is not to have parrots or pigeons about the house. For treatment of the disease, the antibiotics chloromycetin and aureomycin are apparently effective. It is only against these large Rickettsiae that antibiotics are effective; they seem to have little or no effect on the small viruses.

Before closing this short account of some common viruses

affecting animals, mention should be made of the important virus which causes foot-and-mouth disease in cattle. In these days of world shortage of meat, the constant necessity to slaughter whole herds, some of them pedigree, to stop the spread of this disease is a matter of great importance. This policy of slaughter, which is practised in Great Britain though not on the Continent, has frequently been criticised but the result has justified the policy. It is often asked why it is that a vaccine cannot be produced which would give immunity to the animal and thus avoid the expensive remedy of slaughtering all infected animals and their contacts. The chief reason why a vaccine is not produced is the same as in the case of influenza, the existence of several types of virus which do not immunise against each other. As long ago as 1922, two French workers, Vallée and Carré, showed that there existed at least two virus types which they called the O and A types. Seven years later, two other workers, Waldmann and Trautwein, demonstrated a third type known as C. In addition three new types have recently been identified from material from African outbreaks.

The existence of these different virus types, therefore, makes it very difficult to obtain a vaccine which would confer immunity against them all.

In England the work on foot-and-mouth disease is concentrated at a special research institute at Pirbright in Surrey, where new methods of study have been developed. When an outbreak of foot-and-mouth disease occurs, it is necessary to find out to which type the virus belongs. This used to be done by the rather expensive method of inoculating the cattle, but later it was discovered that the guinea pig was susceptible, and this animal was used instead. However, since this involved adapting the virus to the guinea pig by many transfers to fresh animals, it was a laborious process. Recently, however, a rapid method of " typing " the virus was discovered in this country, and later modified in Germany, and at Pirbright, by means of what is called the " complement fixation test." This is a kind of delicate colour test carried out by serological means, and it enables the type of virus involved to be determined within a few hours.

Until recently, the standard method of preparing vaccines has been to infect cattle under experimental conditions with the virus and then to prepare the vaccine from the infected animal. This was a rather laborious and expensive method. It has now been shown, however, by Frankel, a Dutch worker, that virus can be cultured in the tongues of cattle which have been slaughtered for food and a vaccine prepared from the cultured virus. This method has been tested at Pirbright, and vaccine prepared in this way compared with similar vaccine prepared from artificially infected cattle. The two vaccines were found to be similar in every way. The workers at Pirbright are now investigating another possible source of virus material for vaccine production. These are mouse sucklings, which have already proved fruitful in the study of the so-called Coxackie viruses. Unweaned mice are susceptible to many strains of the foot-and-mouth viruses, and they may prove to be a most useful experimental animal.

The virus of foot-and-mouth disease, which, incidentally, is one of the smallest animal viruses, is very infectious, and the greatest precautions are necessary to confine an outbreak once it has occurred. Besides the slaughter and burning of all infected animals and those with which they have been in contact, all the bedding materials, etc., must be burnt, and the clothes, boots, etc., of the farm workers must be disinfected. There are many ways in which the virus is spread and one of these is by survival in imported meat and offal. For example, except for isolated outbreaks, North America is more or less free of the foot-and-mouth virus. But there was an outbreak of the disease in Southern California in 1929. The infection was first noted in a number of pigs, which were observed to be behaving in a peculiar manner. Actually they were walking on their knees owing to the pain of the vesicles on their feet. The outbreak was finally traced to a steamer which had taken on board a quantity of meat at Buenos Aires; the trimmings of this meat were put into the garbage, which was finally fed to the pigs. It is worth noting that the pigs developed the disease eleven days after eating the garbage, and this is just about the incubation period of the virus.

There is, however, a lack of information as to how some out-breaks first occur. It is not uncommon for attacks to develop on isolated farms which have had apparently no contact with an external source of virus infection. Various theories have been put forward to explain this rather curious phenomenon, and the one that seems to fit most of the facts is the suggestion that the virus is carried on the feet of starlings. There is, indeed, quite a lot of circumstantial evidence which supports this hypothesis. Since the virus of foot-and-mouth disease is capable of retaining infectivity for long periods, it is theoretically possible for a bird to carry infective virus on its feet. Again, the starling is the only British bird which keeps together in such large flocks and for preference feeds in the vicinity of cattle. Furthermore, besides the resident birds there are large numbers of starlings of con-tinental origin, coming from Scandinavia and the neighbouring countries and which spend most of the autumn and winter in Britain. This fact, together with the habit of starlings of travelling from their feeding-places each evening to roost communally, shows that there is ample opportunity for the dissemination of the virus by these birds. However, it has yet to be demonstrated that starlings have in fact infected cattle with foot-and-mouth disease by viruses brought on their feet or bodies.

CHAPTER 7

THE VIRUS DISEASES OF INSECTS

WE HAVE SEEN in Chapter 3 what a large and important part is
played by insects in disseminating both plant and animal viruses,
but we have not yet discussed that other relationship where the
insect is itself attacked by a virus disease. Although such virus
diseases have been known for many years, the systematic study
of insect viruses has been much neglected and only recently has
any intensive work been carried out. This is rather curious
because many of these viruses are of great interest particularly
as regards the extraordinary changes which take place inside the
body of the diseased insect. The *polyhedral diseases*, with which
we are chiefly concerned in this chapter, are so-called because
of the development in the body of the infected insect of huge
numbers of many-sided crystals from which the name " polyhedral disease " is derived. Some of these polyhedral bodies are
shown in Plates XIII and XIV (pp. 120-21).

TYPES OF INSECTS ATTACKED BY VIRUSES

Virus diseases, mainly of the polyhedral variety, have been
recorded from various kinds of insects, especially those belonging
to the Hymenoptera (ants, bees and wasps) and the Lepidoptera
(butterflies and moths). By far the greater number of viruses
have been recorded from the Lepidoptera, though no doubt
with further study other groups of insects will be found to suffer
from similar diseases.

An interesting feature about the polyhedral viruses is that
they seem to attack only the larval stages, the adult insects

Plate V. Crystals, octahedra, of the turnip yellow mosaic virus

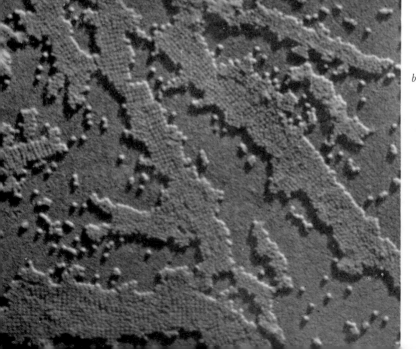

Plate VI. Caption
opposite

apparently being resistant. There is, however, a good deal of evidence, as we shall see later, that the virus can be passed through the female parent and infect the offspring.

Several of these caterpillar diseases have been known for a number of years and they must be only a fraction of the existing viruses. Indeed, experience at Cambridge has shown that if caterpillars are bred on a large scale for some time, a virus disease is likely to turn up sooner or later. This has been the case with five species of tiger moth larvae, four species of the so-called giant tropical silk moths and the currant moth (*Abraxas grossulariata*). None of these viruses have been previously described.

A possible explanation of the sudden appearance of a virus in a group of apparently healthy caterpillars will be discussed later on.

Two of the best-known polyhedral diseases of caterpillars are those attacking the silkworm (*Bombyx mori*) and the nun moth (*Lymantria monacha*). The first of these diseases is usually known as " jaundice " because of the yellow colour assumed by the infected silkworms. The second was given, by the Germans, the peculiar name of " Wipfelkrankheit " or " tree-top " disease. Towards the end of the last century, a tremendous epidemic broke out among the great population of nun moth larvae which were destroying much of the spruce forests of central Europe.

It was noticed that the infected caterpillars tended to migrate to the top of the trees, where they died but remained hanging, attached by their abdominal feet, hence " tree-top " disease. Such dead caterpillars are merely limp sacks, half full of polyhedral bodies.

It has been suggested by way of explanation of this peculiar and characteristic behaviour of the diseased caterpillars that the

---

Plate VIa. Plate-like crystals of a tobacco necrosis virus.

    b. Electron micrograph of a tobacco necrosis virus showing the arrangement of the particles in crystalline form. X 30,000 *approx.*

wholesale migration to the tree-tops might be connected with partial suffocation consequent upon the pressure of the poly-hedral bodies on the fine tracheal breathing tubes. On this assumption the caterpillars make for the tops of the trees, where there are more air currents and the pressure is lower. This is probably not the true explanation, and in any case the pressure would only be lower by an infinitesimal amount.

The rapid disintegration of the internal tissues is typical of these caterpillar viruses and in Plate VIIb (p. 84) may be seen a dead caterpillar of a foreign silk moth (*Automeris io*) hanging by its abdominal feet in the manner characteristic of this type of infection.

How Insect Viruses are Spread About

We have seen in Chapter 3 that viruses which infect plants rely to a great extent upon plant-feeding insects to transport them from plant to plant. In some animal virus diseases, also, yellow fever, for example, an insect plays an essential role in the transmission of the virus. Although we do not yet know very much about the methods of spread of insect viruses, there is no evidence that there is any comparable phenomenon in this case. But one thing is certain about these caterpillar viruses, and that is that they are highly infectious. In the polyhedral diseases, the crystalline polyhedral bodies are not the virus particles themselves as was thought at one time, but they do contain virus as we shall see later. These polyhedra are extremely stable and can be dried whilst still retaining infective virus within them. When they enter the gut of a susceptible caterpillar they are dissolved by the action of the alkaline secretions and the virus particles are liberated. The polyhedra thus act as an extremely efficient kind of parcel post for the distribution of the disease. One method, therefore, by which the caterpillars can become infected is by ingesting the polyhedra while eating leaves con-taminated by other infected caterpillars. The contamination of the food supply and surroundings by polyhedra is ensured by the mode of development of the disease. In some species the infected

caterpillar excretes large quantities of fluid which contains polyhedra (Plate VIIa, p. 84). The faeces, also, are infectious. In the
last stages of the disease, as already pointed out, the caterpillar is
converted into a mere sac filled with polyhedral bodies. The
skin of such caterpillars ruptures very easily, liberating millions
of polyhedra which, being able to withstand drying, spread
infection far and wide.

The efficiency of the method of spread by ingestion of polyhedra, however, seems to vary with the species of caterpillar
and hence with the virus since these viruses are extremely specific
in their action. Thus, it is easy to infect the larva of the currant
moth by moistening the mouth parts with a suspension of polyhedra but less easy to infest some other species in the same
manner.

Another and very important method of propagation of the
polyhedral diseases is by passage of the virus from parent to
offspring, and this is a phenomenon which is comparatively rare
in the virus diseases of plants and the higher animals.

A description of a polyhedral disease as it occurs in the larvae
of the oak silk moth (*Telea polyphemus*) will serve to illustrate some
of these points. When a half-grown caterpillar of this species is
artificially infected with its specific polyhedral virus, either by
ingestion or inoculation, the insect becomes sluggish and ceases
to grow, although it may continue to feed spasmodically for a
time. Frequently, drops of fluid, at first colourless but later
turning black, exude from the body of the animal (see Plate
VIIa). If such drops are examined under the oil immersion lens
of the optical microscope they will be found to contain large
numbers of polyhedral bodies. Sometimes it happens that larvae,
which may become infected when nearing maturity, complete
their larval life, make their cocoon and may even pupate. If,
under these conditions, the cocoon is cut open, the dead larva or
pupa is found full of polyhedral bodies. These remarks apply
to the caterpillar which is actively diseased. Sometimes, however,
it seems clear that the virus may be present in a latent condition
within the caterpillar. There is a good deal of evidence for this;
for example, apparently healthy caterpillars of the oak silk moth

pupated and gave rise to adult moths. From these moths a number of fertile eggs were obtained. Of the caterpillars arising from these eggs a percentage died of polyhedral disease, the age of the caterpillars varying from several weeks to a few hours. Examination of the caterpillars which died shortly after emerging from the eggs showed that they contained large numbers of polyhedral bodies. This is interesting because it indicates that the virus must have passed from the mother to the developing embryo and was not carried mechanically on the outside of the egg. It is hardly feasible to suppose that so many polyhedra could have developed within a few hours of hatching if infection had been derived from the outside of the egg at the moment of emergence of the young larva.

Further evidence of the transmission of virus through the egg and of its persistence in a latent condition is given by some breeding experiments with the garden tiger moth (*Arctia caja*). Some hundreds of caterpillars of this species were bred in the laboratory in a room where no tiger moth had ever been previously kept. The caterpillars which were perfectly healthy were bred continuously through four generations without going through a diapause (resting period). In the fifth generation a polyhedral disease developed and wiped out the entire stock of caterpillars. It seems clear, therefore, that these polyhedral viruses must be capable of lying latent within the body of a susceptible caterpillar, being passed from one generation to another until, under some stimulus the nature of which is at present unknown, the virus begins active multiplication and gives rise to a disease. It is possible that careful examination of the tissues of apparently normal caterpillars, and even of the adult insects, by means of the electron microscope may yield further knowledge on those latent infections.

Changes taking place inside the Diseased Caterpillars

The polyhedral diseases of insects are sometimes referred to as " nuclear diseases " because the pathological changes seem to start inside the cell nucleus. Whether all polyhedral diseases begin inside the cell nucleus is not certain: it may be that in some cases the focus of multiplication is in the cell cytoplasm. At all events there is no question but that at some stage in the polyhedral disease these curious many-sided crystals start to form inside the nuclei of susceptible cells.

If a section is cut through an infected larva of the currant moth (*Abraxas grossulariata*), and then examined on the optical microscope, it will be seen that the cell nuclei are enormously enlarged. Furthermore, they exhibit a kind of " honeycomb " structure which is due to the fact that they are packed with polyhedral crystals.

The nuclear membrane must be extremely elastic, judging by the expansion caused by the pressure of the polyhedral bodies contained within it. However, the nucleus eventually bursts, liberating the crystals into the surrounding cytoplasm. As the disease progresses, the cells also disintegrate until the caterpillar ends up in the characteristic condition shown in Plate VIIb, p. 84.

THE NATURE OF THE POLYHEDRAL BODIES

The significance of the polyhedral bodies in relation to the virus itself has long been sought. For a time they were thought to be some kind of organism causing the disease and were given names like *Crystalloplasma polyedricum* and *Chlamydozoon prowazeki*. It was not, however, until quite recently that it was shown that these bodies which, incidentally, appear to be genuine crystals, were not the infective agents themselves, but contained some virus inside them (Bergold, 1947).

If a polyhedral body is dissolved in weak sodium carbonate and the process examined under the high power of the optical microscope with dark ground illumination, an interesting phenomenon can be observed. Each polyhedral body is enveloped in a kind of skin or membrane, and as the substance of the crystal dissolves, numbers of highly refractive dots can be seen vibrating violently inside the membrane. Occasionally one or two pass right out of the membrane and disappear. These highly refractive dots appear to be the virus particles themselves, which are too small to be resolved by the optical microscope and so appear under the dark field as bright points of light as they are driven about inside the enclosing membrane by Brownian movement.

A much clearer picture of what happens when the polyhedral body is dissolved can be obtained by means of the electron microscope. In Plate XIIIb (p. 120) is shown an electron micrograph taken by Dr. R. W. G. Wyckoff. In it can be seen the collapsed membrane which enclosed the polyhedral body before it was dissolved in weak alkali. The rod-shaped virus particles which have been liberated can be clearly seen. This particular polyhedral body came from an infected caterpillar of the scarlet tiger moth (*Panaxia dominula*), and well-defined virus rods are always present in this disease. Whilst many of the polyhedral viruses of insects seem to have rod-shaped particles, it does not follow that all viruses of this type are rod-shaped. For example, when the polyhedra from virus-infected caterpillars of the garden tiger moth (*Arctia caja*) or the cream spot tiger moth (*A. villaca*) are treated with weak sodium carbonate the result is very different. Instead of the polyhedral body dissolving away completely, as it does in the case of the scarlet tiger moth, there remains a shell pitted with a large number of holes of very uniform diameter (Plate XIV, p. 121). Surrounding these disintegrated polyhedra there can sometimes be seen clusters of spherical bodies which have about the same diameter as the holes. The same sort of pitting is visible when undissolved polyhedra from these two species are sectioned and photographed on the electron microscope. Another point of difference between these two types of polyhedral bodies is the apparent lack of an enveloping membrane in the case of those polyhedra which do not contain virus rods. It seems likely, therefore, that the virus diseases of caterpillars, which produce crystalline polyhedral inclusions fall into at least two groups, those with rod-shaped, and those with spoherical, virus particles (Smith and Wyckoff, 1950).

It will be realised from this brief description of the polyhedral bodies that there is much yet to be learned about their function. We know that they are protein crystals, but of a different protein from the virus particles themselves, and that they contain, in some diseases, about 3-5 per cent of virus.

But what is the purpose of the crystals and why is each crystal enclosed in a membrane? Again, how do the virus rods get inside the crystal? Are they occluded during the growth of the crystal? It does not seem possible for them to form inside a solid. At the moment we have no answers to these questions.

Do the Insect Viruses occur in more than one Form?

By means of the electron microscope much information has been obtained on the shape and appearance of the actual particles of insect viruses. Photographs taken with the electron microscope of the comparatively large virus of influenza show the particles to be mainly of a spherical nature, but there also occur, from time to time, much larger, elongated structures. It has been suggested that these different particles may conceivably be stages in some kind of a life-cycle. Bergold (1950), who has done much pioneer work on the virus diseases of insects, considers that possibly a similar state of affairs exists with the insect viruses, which are also comparatively large, since he has been able to photograph different kinds of virus particles which may be part of a developmental cycle. Bergold postulates a rather complicated system of multiplication somewhat on the following lines. The virus appears first as a minute spherical body or " germ," which increases in size and develops into an elongated curved body surrounded by a membrane. Later the virus particle straightens out, ruptures the membrane and appears as the rod-shaped particle characteristic of many insect viruses. It is thought that this rod-shaped particle contains several smaller sub-units, each of which develops into a rod.

If this theory of a development cycle is confirmed by further investigation, it will be most important and interesting, because it suggests that these rather large insect viruses may be organisms of a nature hitherto unknown.

CAN VIRUS DISEASES BE USED TO CONTROL INSECT PESTS?

We know that natural outbreaks of polyhedral diseases occur from time to time in the great infestations of gypsy moth and nun moth caterpillars in forests in central Europe. When this happens, the infestation dies down and it may be several years before the numbers of caterpillars build up again. When one of these virus epidemics is in progress, the number of polyhedral bodies produced is so great that they form a fine white dust on the ground and the surrounding trees. It seems logical to deduce, therefore, that by the large-scale production and dissemination of caterpillar viruses some degree of control of outbreaks of injurious insects might be achieved. This possibility is being investigated at the present time in several countries.

In Quebec much defoliation of the spruce trees has been caused by a sawfly larva. The outbreak of larvae commenced in 1930 and reached its peak several years later, about 1938. After that, the outbreak declined until in 1940 it had practically disappeared. Balch and Bird (1944), two Candian workers, consider that this decline coincided with the development of a polyhedral disease among the sawfly larvae, and they offer some interesting evidence in support of this conclusion. Their method of recording the effect of the disease was to count the number of larvae which reached the sixth stage without being infected. When the larvae reach this stage they stop feeding and drop to the ground to spin their cocoons. Balch and Bird counted the number of such healthy larvae which dropped to the ground on a given plot during the years 1939-41. One example is as follows: in 1938 the total number of healthy larvae dropping from the trees was 1389; in the following three years the numbers were respectively 465, 19 and 2 larvae. It has been calculated that the percentage mortality in the plot ranged from 94.8 per cent one year to 99.7 per cent during the next three years.

By introducing extracts of dried diseased larvae into Newfoundland, the disease was established there, where previously it had been unknown.

In Canada, also, a virus has been discovered affecting the spruce budworm, a small caterpillar which causes great damage to the spruce forests. Efforts are being made to propagate this virus disease on a large scale, but at the moment its efficacy seems doubtful.

In California, some experiments have been made, using a polyhedral virus against the caterpillars of the alfalfa (lucerne) butterfly. Huge quantities of polyhedra were obtained for this purpose, both by breeding large numbers of caterpillars and infecting them with the virus and by collecting quantities of caterpillars already infected naturally in the field. It was found that application of a virus suspension, containing 150 million polyhedra per fluid ounce, at the rate of five gallons per acre, was adequate to ensure infection of a field population of larvae and to reduce its numbers below an economic level, at all events under conditions obtaining in the northern San Joaquin Valley. Furthermore, it was found that this artificially induced disease was capable of starting an epidemic even where the numbers of caterpillars were small, and, moreover, of starting it much earlier in the season than it would occur naturally. Application by means of a small aeroplane was found to be the most convenient method of treating large fields with a virus suspension. Small fields would be more suited to application by ground equipment (Thompson and Steinhaus, 1950).

Finally, to come nearer home, some attempts are being made in this country to control that familiar insect, the common clothes moth, by similar means. The larva of the common clothes moth is susceptible to a polyhedral virus of the same nature as those already mentioned and which, like them, is extremely infectious. So far, the attempts to control the clothes moth have been only on a small scale and in enclosed spaces, but, so far as they go, they have been very successful. One experiment on these lines was as follows: a horse rug heavily infested with the larvae of the clothes moth was put in a large chest and sprayed with a suspension of polyhedra. After about a month the chest was opened and large numbers of larvae were observed on the surface of the rug instead of being hidden in the cloth. Closer examinations revealed that the larvae all showed the milky appearance characteristic of the disease and were, in fact, in a moribund condition. Very few healthy larvae could be found.

There are two main advantages of a polyhedral virus over an insecticide such as D.D.T. as a means of control. First, it is much more persistent since it remains infectious for a year or even longer, and secondly, it is self-propagating in the sense that it is passed from larva to larva, multiplying all the time.

The disadvantages, as with any biological control method, are the possibility of the adaptation of the parasite to its host so that the latter becomes a symptomless carrier, and also the necessity for the epidemics to be of some size if they are to be effective.

References

BALCH, R. E., and BIRD, F. T. (1944). A disease of the European spruce sawfly, *Gilpiniia hercyniae* (Htg.), and its place in natural control. *Sci. Agric. 25*: 65-80.

BERGOLD, G. H. (1947). Die Isolierung des Polyeder-Virus und die Natur der Polyeder. *Z. f. Naturforsch. 2b*: 122-43.

BERGOLD, G. H. (1950). The multiplication of insect viruses as organisms. *Canadian Journ. Res. E. 28*: 5-11.

SMITH, KENNETH M., and WYCKOFF, R. W. G. (1950). Structure within polyhedra associated with insect virus diseases. *Nature, London, 166*: 861.

THOMPSON, C. G., and STEINHAUS, E. A. (1950). Further tests using a polyhedrosis virus to control the alfalfa caterpillar. *Hilgardia, 19*: 411-45.

CHAPTER 8

VIRUSES AND TUMOURS

IT IS UNNECESSARY for us to emphasise here the importance of malignant tumours and their possible causation by viruses. As the reader will see a little later, a number of indubitable tumours are caused by viruses, but the theory that malignant tumours generally, including human cancer, are due to virus infection is not universally accepted. If it were, in the words of the British Medical Journal, " Of the current theories of the nature of cancer, some 90 per cent could be quietly relegated to the waste-paper basket, leaving investigators free to concentrate on a much more limited field through which certain obvious paths are clearly indicated."

Virus tumours have been described affecting a variety of very different kinds of organisms, including plants, insects, frogs, fowls (Frontispiece) and rabbits, but not man, except *Condyloma acuminatum*, or venereal warts which may become malignant.

Before we discuss these carcinogenic viruses it will be well to consider some of the outstanding theories of the cause of malignant growths which are held at the present time. Certain classes of chemicals, hydro carbons, contain a substance which is carcinogenic, that is, when applied to the skin, it gives rise to malignant tumours in animals. Chimney-sweep's cancer and mule-spinner's cancer are examples of this. Tar is another carcinogen and also certain forms of dust, such as that from tarred roads; silica and iron oxide are under suspicion of causing lung tumours if inhaled. Also many substances occurring in traces as impurities in chemicals used in industry are carcinogenic. X-rays which are used to cure cancer can also cause it, and the gamma rays, given off by atomic fission, produce a disease of the blood, leukaemia, which is a form of cancer. There is also the case of tumours of the bladder caused by an ingredient present at one time in too great quantities in lipsticks.

Now the fact that these carcinogenic substances exist is often brought forward as evidence against the theory of virus causation. This, however, is not necessarily true: it may only imply that the carcinogen is the stimulating factor or " trigger " to virus action. A necessary corollary to this " trigger action," of course, is the existence in the cell of a latent virus or viruses. Such latent viruses would have to be very widely distributed in the animal kingdom, but there is no especial difficulty in accepting that suggestion. Examples of the occurrence of latent viruses in man are *herpes simplex* or " cold sores " in large numbers of the population, the polyhedral viruses in insects, the X virus in potato plants and the lysogenic bacteria which carry a latent virus. Mice also seem to carry latent viruses which can be stimulated into action by serial passages—that is, progressive transfer of the virus from mouse to mouse. Perhaps the strongest evidence for this theory is the production of the so-called " tar sarcomata " in fowls. In certain cases it has been shown that the application of tar to the skin of fowls produces a malignant growth which is then transmissible in series to other non-tarred fowls. Of this phenomenon Rous (1943) suggests that the carcinogens have in common an ability to play upon the tumour-forming potentialities of the cells, with the result that these become realities. The potentialities themselves may be viruses incapable of causing growths unless the local conditions happen to be right or are made right, and even then perhaps only as the result of virus variation.

Not all tar sarcomata of fowls have been shown to contain a virus, but it is interesting to find that some of these have shown a serological relationship to the Rous No. 1 sarcoma, which is a definite virus tumour.

The behaviour of a carcinogen such as tar in conjunction with a tumour-forming virus is both interesting and dramatic. In the case of the infectious fibroma virus of rabbits, sarcoma-like lesions are formed in the infected animal, but these usually regress after a few weeks. If, however, the skin of the rabbit is treated with tar, the regression is delayed, sometimes indefinitely, and frequently the tumours become invasive and fatal. Similarly with the rabbit papilloma virus which produces warts on the tar, the skin of rabbits: if the ears are previously treated with virus becomes localised in the treated areas and produces vigorous growths which may be malignant from the start. This behaviour does not occur with any other virus, such as vaccinia, which might be present, but only with tumour-forming viruses.

In his discussion of latent viruses and tumours, Andrewes (1939) considers that such latent indigenous viruses and their hosts where neither does harm to the other, are examples of perfect parasitism. He says: " Cancer when it occurs in animals, would then be due to the incursion of some unexpected factor, a *tertium quid*, which broke up the happy association; a disease affecting both partners, of advantage to neither. Instead of a disease of man caused by a virus, we should then have to consider human cancer as a disease of the man-virus partnership."

This is basically the conception of a virus, tumour-inducing or otherwise, as a parasitic organism and differs fundamentally from the theory put forward by Darlington (1948), who favours the idea of the *de novo* origin of viruses. He suggests that cancer can be ascribed to mutations in cytoplasmic determinants, indifferently infectious or non-infectious, which make themselves known by causing the resumption of growth. Three types of particles are postulated which are conditional and interchangeable. Cancer-producing particles fall into all three categories. These are the hereditary plasmagenes, the proviruses, and the naturally infectious viruses or viruses proper.

The plasmagenes are self-propagating particles, transmitted by heredity but lying outside the nucleus, and they are known in many groups of organisms. As examples of infectious plasmagenes, Darlington quotes the transfer in *Paramecium* during coitus of the *Kappa plasmagene* or death factor from one individual to its mate. This has recently, however, been shown to be a rickettsia, which is a type of disease agent larger than the average virus, and in this case can be cured by the antibiotic, aureomycin.

Similarly, transplantation of an organ or of serum from a carbon dioxide-sensitive *Drosophila* fly infects a non-sensitive fly, including its egg, with the sensitive plasmagene.

On the question of proviruses we feel somewhat uncertain. Darlington defines them as self-propagating particles which in plants are not transmitted from one host to another in nature but only by artificial methods. They are normally transmitted by heredity but have the properties necessary for natural infection if an infective agent or vector were to come along. Now there seem to us to be very few agents which fall into this category. The virus of paracrinkle present in all potatoes of the ' King Edward ' variety, which does not apparently spread in nature, used to be the most quoted example. But this has now been shown to be transmissible by sap-inoculation to tomatoes. The only other example of which we have knowledge is the so-called rubberiness of ' Lord Lambourne ' apple trees.

However, if the fact that the potato paracrinkle virus is sap-transmissible does not disqualify it as a provirus, then there are many other plant viruses which could be placed alongside it. These are viruses which have been isolated, usually from a single plant, have no known insect vector or other natural method of spread, but *are* transmissible by mechanical methods of sap-inoculation. These might be called " laboratory viruses " since, had they not been preserved in the laboratory, they would have disappeared with the death of the original infected plant. Most of these viruses, but not all, have appeared once and have not been observed again. Examples are the viruses of tomato bushy stunt, tomato black ring, *Arabis* mosaic, lovage mosaic, tobacco broken ringspot and the mangold local lesion virus. Unlike the paracrinkle virus, all these viruses have a very wide host range. However, so far as we know, none of the " laboratory viruses " quoted here, including that of paracrinkle, are " normally transmitted by heredity."

We have, then, briefly stated the case for the virus origin of tumours, whether we regard the virus as arising within the cells or arriving from outside as a parasitic organism.

There is, however, still a school of thought which agrees with Paul Ehrlich's somewhat pontifical pronouncement: " Until some fundamental discovery is made revealing the nature of life itself, not a step forward will be made in our knowledge of cancer."

Growth stimulation in plants caused by virus infection is common enough when it takes the form of organised growth, the most familiar being the production of small leaves or *enations* on the underside of another leaf (Plate II, p. 37). Unorganised growth stimulated by viruses is much less common, but there are one or two instances of what appear to be true virus tumours or neoplasms in plants. The most striking example is that of a virus affecting leguminous plants known as the wound tumour virus and first described by Black (1945). The virus, which is not mechanically transmissible, is carried by certain specific insect vectors, the leaf-hoppers *Agalliopsis novella* and *Agallia constricta*. Although the virus usually invades the whole plant, the tumours are local in character. Observations show that wounds play an important part in starting the growth of the tumours in the diseased plant. Thus growths are most prevalent on the roots close to the lateral roots, which always cause small wounds in the mother roots from which they emerge. Similarly, tumours are liable to arise exactly at the spot where a stem may be in contact with the rim of the pot in which the plant is growing, and where there is likely to be a small wound caused by such contact (Plate III, p. 52). Heredity of the host also seems to play a part in determining the tumour reaction. For example, Black prepared six groups of plants where the plants in each group were propagated vegetatively and were thus genetically identical. When the plants were infected with the virus it was found that the tumour reaction within each clone was very uniform, but that the reaction in different clones varied from a mild infection with very minute tumours to very severe infection with masses of tumours on the roots. Age of the tissue also seems to play a part in tumour formation. The actual formation of the tumours has been observed by Kelly and Black (1949). The tumours arise chiefly in the pericycle region of roots and stems. They enlarge by cell division rather than by increase in cell size. The phloem is the first tissue to differentiate at the base of the tumour, and shortly after xylem differentiation follows at the periphery. Growth of the tumour continues by means of cell divisions in the meristematic tissue between the xylem and phloem, and between the xylem extensions. No evidence of metastases, the breaking away of tumour cells to form tumours at another site, has been observed.

The question that remains to be answered is why one cell in the pericycle of an infected root develops into an organised lateral root whilst another apparently similar cell develops into an unorganised tumour. There is no evidence of the pre-existence of different potentially cancerous cells, and most of the cells must equally contain virus.

The only other plant virus known at present to cause tumours is one affecting sugar-cane and causing the so-called Fiji disease. The swellings which develop in an affected plant are elongated and occur on the under-surface of the leaves. They extend along the larger veins or vascular bundles and are, in fact, formed by the abnormal growth of the tissues comprising these bundles. Swellings are produced in a similar manner in the vascular bundles of the stem and may be detected by splitting open the stick of an affected shoot. The swellings always originate in the phloem and are caused by the proliferation of the phloem cells and occasionally of cells in the surrounding tissue.

The virus is not transmissible by mechanical sap-inoculation but is carried by a specific insect vector.

Although the two plant virus tumour diseases which we have briefly discussed are the only examples of this type known at present, there is a third interesting plant tumour which should be included in our discussion for comparison. It has been known for many years that an outgrowth, known as crown gall, was produced in many plants by inoculation with the bacterium, *Phytomonas tumefaciens*. Within the last few years, however, it has been shown by two American workers (White and Braun, 1941)

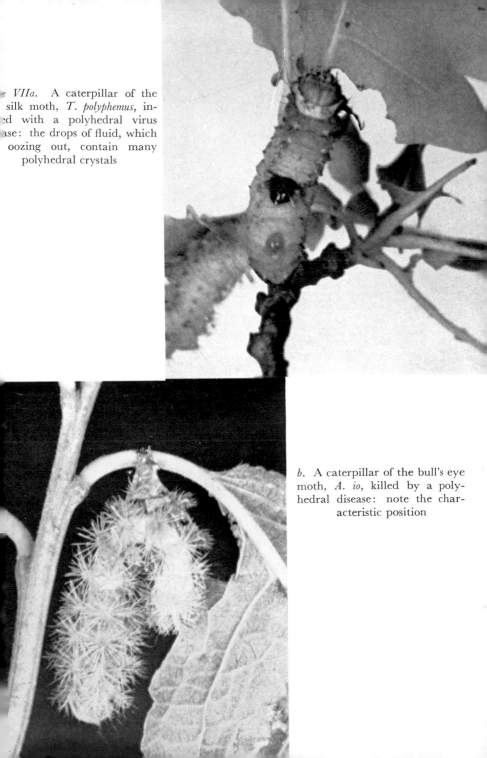

VIIa. A caterpillar of the silk moth, *T. polyphemus,* in-d with a polyhedral virus ase: the drops of fluid, which oozing out, contain many polyhedral crystals

b. A caterpillar of the bull's eye moth, *A. io,* killed by a poly-hedral disease: note the char-acteristic position

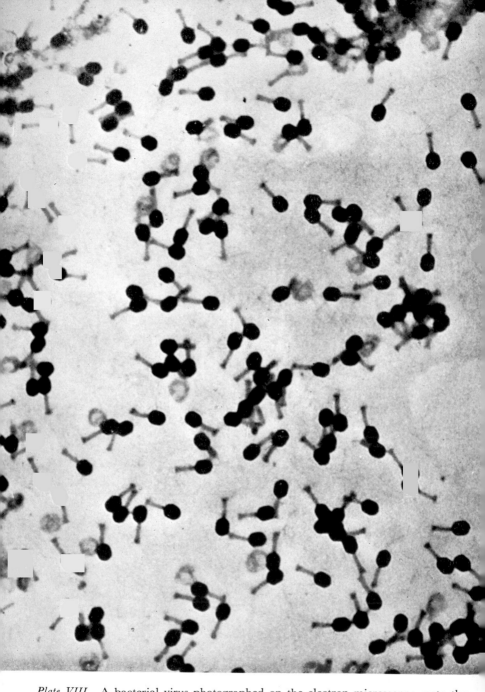

Plate VIII. A bacterial virus photographed on the electron microscope: note the characteristic tadpole-like shape (X 20,000) (*after Sharp*)

that the secondary tumours which develop near the site of inoculation are frequently free of all bacteria. Furthermore, if these secondary tumours are transplanted into a fresh susceptible host they will grow and give rise to new tumours indistinguishable from the tumours from which they were originally derived. This behaviour seems to have become an intimate function of the cells themselves quite independent of any further bacterial stimulation. The tumours can be grown in tissue culture fluids for long periods, and when implanted into new plants will give rise to fresh tumours. These bacteria-free tumour tissues have now retained their tumour-inducing capacity for more than five years. There has therefore been a change in the nature of the cell, a change which is the fundamental problem in crown gall, the wound tumour disease and in neoplastic diseases of animals. De Ropp (1947) considers that in the light of existing knowledge it is not possible to come to any conclusion on the nature of the tumefacient agent in crown gall. He suggests the different categories into which the agent might fall.

(1) A simple carcinogenic substance analogous to methylcholanthrene or dibenzanthracene. If such a substance did exist in bacteria-free crown gall tissues it should be possible to extract it and to obtain tumours in normal tissue by application of the extract.

(2) A carcinogenic virus, similar to the wound tumour virus or the Rous fowl sarcoma virus, which was invariably associated with the bacterium *Phytomonas tumefaciens* but which was capable of continuing its existence apart from the bacteria in the plant cell, the metabolism of which it profoundly affects. It is worth noting here that a wound is also essential for a tumour to be produced in the presence of *P. tumefaciens* just as it was in the case of the wound tumour virus.

Incidentally, attempts to produce tumours by inoculation with the ground-up tissue of crown gall which contained no whole cells have failed. This does not necessarily rule out the possibility of a virus as there are many authentic viruses which cannot be transmitted in this way. It is also interesting to note that the tumour-inducing principle of crown gall is inactivated at a temperature of 32° C. In other words, normal cells may be transformed to tumour cells at a temperature of 25° C. but not at 32° C. Once the cellular transformation has been accomplished the tumour cells develop into a neoplastic growth at both temperatures (Braun and Mandle, 1948).

(3) A factor of the " plasmagene " or " cancer protein " type. These may be compared with the proviruses of Darlington, and the situation here, visualised is little different from that postulated in the case of tar and other similar substances. In this case presumably the bacterium, *P. tumefaciens*, acts as the carcinogen and either alters some already existing substance in the cell into a self-perpetuating tumefacient entity, or stimulates into action an already existing self-perpetuating substance, in other words, a latent virus.

An interesting tumour caused by a virus in an insect has recently been described by Bird (1949). The virus is one of the polyhedral type which we have discussed in Chap. 7, and the insect concerned is the spruce sawfly, *Gilpina hercyniae*. In the diseased larva, the virus affects only the digestive cells of the mid-gut epithelium. After infection has taken place and when the characteristic polyhedral bodies are appearing, in the nuclei abnormal cell proliferations appear in the regions of the regenerative *nidi*. These latter are replacement cells which may be scattered singly along the gut as in caterpillars or collected at intervals in small groups or nidi.

When the abnormal cell proliferations develop, there is no increase in the size of the nidi, but a few cells are apparently released which multiply rapidly to form the proliferations. Large tumours are formed only when the larva becomes infected just prior to the last larval moult, when all the materials necessary for further metamorphosis are accumulated. If larvae become infected at an earlier stage, death from the effect of the disease prevents the formation of very large tumours. There seems to be no evidence of infiltration of the tumour cells into any other organ in the spruce sawfly. All the evidence suggests that the tumours are non-malignant.

Lucké (1938), working at the University of Pennsylvania, has described a tumour, apparently caused by a virus, in the kidney of the leopard frog (*Rana pipiens*). This is rather unusual since tumours are rare in the more primitive cold-blooded vertebrates, and it is interesting because its cell nuclei frequently contain large inclusions which are characteristic of some animal virus diseases such as herpes, for example. More than 600 tumours have been examined and Lucké describes them as either solitary or multiple and occurring in one or both kidneys. They vary in size from small nodules to large irregular masses, several times the size of the kidney which they replace. All gradations occur between the frankly malignant and destructive, and the benign or non-malignant types. The neoplastic disease, once established, appears to be progressive, for tumours with evidence of recession are uncommon.

Inoculations of living fragments or cell suspensions of tumour into the lymph sacs, or cranial cavity of the healthy frogs produced no local tumours, but in 20 per cent of inoculated frogs which survived six months, kidney tumours developed. This, of course, is a far higher percentage than occurred in the control untreated frogs. A similar result was obtained with dried material and once also with glycerinated tumour. Inoculations into frogs of a different species produced no result.

These experiments suggest that the kidney tumour is caused by an organ-specific virus although experiments with a sterile filtrate do not appear to have been carried out.

Turning now from frogs to mice, we find that these little animals are prone to tumours of many kinds, mammary cancers, lung tumours, leukaemia, bone tumours, etc., but the one which is most relevant to this discussion is the breast cancer of mice described by Bittner (1936) and which is thought to be caused by a virus.

Some strains of mice used in cancer research have been found to have a very high incidence of breast cancer, sometimes as high as 80-90 per cent, whereas in other strains the disease is very rare. Bittner found that in hybrids between these two strains, the incidence of breast cancer in the offspring depended entirely upon whether the mother came from a high or low cancer family, and was also not dependent upon the Mendelian laws of heredity. In other words, the liability to mammary cancer is handed down through the mother. This observation led to experiments in which the young of a strain of mice with a high natural incidence of breast cancer were suckled from birth by mice from another strain with a low cancer incidence. These mice were saved from developing breast cancer later on.

The reciprocal experiment in which sucklings of low cancer strains were fostered by females of high cancer strains gave less dramatic results. Rous suggests that there may be some impediment present in the low cancer strain which renders the " milk-influence " relatively ineffective. It is now thought by many workers that this " milk-influence " or " milk-factor " is a virus.

There is no evidence yet that inoculation of the supposed virus after extraction from a breast tumour will provoke a tumour directly. It has to be introduced into suckling mice and they must become adults before it will induce tumour formation; it may in fact lie latent in one generation but yet be transmitted to the next generation with the eventual development of mammary cancers.

The first malignant virus tumour to be discovered in an animal was in 1910, a sarcoma in the domestic fowl, usually called the Rous sarcoma, after its discoverer, Peyton Rous. He found the original tumour in the subcutaneous tissue of the breast of an adult pure-bred hen. The other individuals of the stock were healthy, and although susceptible normal chickens and chickens with the tumour were kept together, no instance of the spontaneous transmission of the growth ever occurred.

The tumour is easily transplanted from one fowl to another, and the inoculation into the breast muscle of a piece of tumour tissue one millimetre in diameter may give rise in the course of a week to a growing nodule 1·5 centimetres broad. On the other hand, the tumours which result from injection of a cell-free filtrate take much longer to appear. It may be as long as three weeks before any reaction takes place, then one or two very small, shot-like bodies appear which soon develop into the characteristic mass. At first, repeated attempts to transfer the tumour to chickens of another stock, which resembled the original tumour stock but which were probably not pure bred, were unsuccessful. Later the sarcomata seemed to increase in malignancy and gained the power to grow in chickens of other kinds. They could never, however, be transmitted to birds of other species or to mammals.

An interesting phenomenon is the effect of repeated transplantations on the behaviour of the resulting tumours. The rate of growth increased so much that growths ten or twelve centimetres in length by six in width would develop three weeks after inoculation of a piece of neoplastic tissue only two millimetres in diameter and often death of the fowl ensued within 26-30 days from the date of inoculation. Metastasis is common, and it is thought that the metastases result from the distribution of tumour cells by way of the blood.

Young fowls are the most easily infected and healthy, wellnourished birds prove more susceptible than the thin and ill. Indeed, illness of the host may cause temporary regression of the sarcoma. This increased susceptibility of young and healthy birds to infection finds its parallel in infection with the plant viruses where young, rapidly growing seedlings are always used because of their susceptibility. Similarly with the polyhedral viruses of insects, which can infect only the young and immature stages.

Before concluding this brief account of virus tumours, we must mention two more such virus tumours in another mammal besides the mouse, in this case a rabbit. These two tumourforming viruses attack rabbits in America and both have been described by Shope. The first virus induces a disease known as infectious fibroma and the second induces infectious papillomatosis.

The tumours of the fibroma disease are soft and rubbery in the early stages with small firmer nodules in their substance. As they increase in size, they become more solid and develop into firm, usually lobulated tumours. After reaching a maximum size on the tenth or twelfth day after infection, the sub-cutaneous tumours commence to regress and as a rule have completely regressed within 35 days of infection. The tumours seem to be benign and cause little or no ill-effect on the rabbit unless they are very large.

The disease was found occurring naturally in the wild cottontail rabbit in the U.S.A. and was easily transmissible to the domestic rabbit. Shope demonstrated that the fibroma was due to a virus by his inoculation experiments with bacteriologically sterile filtrates. Tumour tissue was minced and ground up in a mortar with sterile sand and suspended in a broth at pH 7·3. The suspension was cleared of coarse particles by centifugation and filtered through Berkefeld V and N filters. All the filtrates were bacteriologically sterile, and when inoculated into a rabbit produced a tumour at the site of inoculation. The filtrates took about two days longer to produce a reaction than the control inoculations with unfiltered suspensions.

It is interesting to find that after a tumour had developed and regressed, the rabbit was resistant to further infection with the tumour virus. It is, however, necessary that a tumour should have actually formed for immunity to be conferred. Curiously enough, infection with the fibroma virus conferred immunity or, at least, resistance, against another fatal virus disease of rabbits known as myxoma, thus suggesting that the two viruses may be related.

The infectious papillomatosis is very common in cottontail rabbits in Kansas, U.S.A., where about one in every twelve animals trapped is infected. The warts or papillomas on the skin vary in size and may be quite small or large onion-shaped or ragged growths. The number of warts on individual animals varies, though exceptional cases have occurred where the body was entirely covered with warts, enough, in fact, to fill a 200-ml. flask. The warts are most commonly found on the thighs, abdomen, neck and shoulders; they are black or greyish-black in colour, well keratinised, and the upper surfaces are frequently irregular or fissured. In section, the average wart has a white or pinkish-white fleshy centre, whilst the upper portion and its lateral surfaces are greyish-black and keratinised. The lateral surfaces of the warts appear vertically striated because each individual wart is composed of closely-packed and almost homogeneous vertical strands of tissue. This vertical striation is particularly evident in cut sections of the warts. The warts are loosely attached to the skin and are easily knocked or pulled off. Affected animals show no loss in weight and are free of any clinical evidence of illness.

Although the papilloma virus is transmissible from the cottontail to the domestic rabbit and forms the characteristic warts, it is very difficult to demonstrate the existence of the virus in these warts by direct methods. In other words, it appears that in the domestic rabbit the papilloma virus is masked.

The virus is filterable through Berkefeld V. N. and W. filters. The usual method of artificial infection is by dropping the infectious fluid on to a patch of skin which has been lightly scarified by a needle or a piece of coarse sandpaper.

It is interesting to find that if the skin of a rabbit is treated, before inoculation with the papilloma virus, with certain chemicals such as methylcholanthrene in benzene or turpentine and acetone, the papillomas appear earlier and in greater number than on untreated skin and the virus is present in greater concentration. The effect of these substances is apparently to cause changes in the skin which bring young, actively regenerating cells into association with the virus in much greater number than ordinarily and in a shorter time. This gives the virus the maximum opportunities for infection and multiplication. Indeed it is possible, by this treatment, to demonstrate the presence of virus which could not be shown to exist with ordinary inoculation methods. In other words, these chemicals may act like carcinogens and prepare the way for the tumour-forming virus (Friedewald, 1942).

Shope found that animals which were carrying warts were rendered completely or partially resistant to reinfection, but there was no apparent relationship between the papilloma virus and those of fibroma or myxoma.

We may appropriately close this short account of virus tumours by the following quotation from Rous (1943):

" With so much uncertain, it is easy to suppose all tumours

to be due to viruses; yet it may be easier than it is wise. When the role of bacteria in disease first reached recognition, much was referred to their action which has since turned out to be of quite other cause. Events are already taking the same course with viruses."

References

ANDREWES, C. H. (1939). Latent virus infections and their possible relevance to the cancer problem. *Proc. Roy. Soc. Med. 33*: 75-86.

BIRD, F. T. (1949). Tumours associated with a virus infection in an insect. *Nature, London, 163*: 777.

BITTNER, J. G. (1936). Some possible effects of nursing on the mammary gland tumour incidence in mice. *Science, 84*: 162.

BLACK, L. M. (1945). A virus tumour disease of plants. *Amer. J. Bot. 32*: 408-15.

BRAUN, A. C., and MANDLE, R. J. (1948). Studies on the inactivation of the tumour-inducing principle in crown gall. *Growth, 12*: 255-69.

DARLINGTON, C. D. (1948). The plasmagene theory of the origin of cancer. *Brit. J. Cancer, 2*: 118.

DE ROPP, R. S. (1947). The isolation and behaviour of bacteria-free crown-gall tissue from primary galls of *Helianthus annuus*. *Phytopath, 37*: 201-06.

FRIEDEWALD, W. F. (1942). Cell state as affecting susceptibility to a virus. *J. Exp. Med. 75*: 197.

KELLY, S. B., and BLACK, L. M. (1949). The origin, development and cell structure of a virus tumour in plants. *Amer. J. Bot. 36*: 65-73.

LUCKÈ, B. A. (1938). Carcinoma in the leopard frog: its probable causation by a virus. *J. Exp. Med. 68*: 457.

ROUS, P. (1943), *in* Virus Diseases. Cornell Univ. Press. Ithaca, New York.

SHOPE, R. E. (1932). A transmissible tumour-like condition in rabbits. *J. Exp. Med. 56*: 793.

SHOPE, R. E. (1933). Infectious papillomatosis of rabbits. *J. Exp. Med. 58*: 607.

WHITE P. R., and BRAUN, A. C. (1941). Crown gall production by bacteria-free tumour tissues. *Science, 94*: 239-41.

CHAPTER 9

ISOLATION OF VIRUSES

THERE IS LIABLE to be confusion in the mind of the layman in his conception of a virus disease, particularly in plants, because of his failure to differentiate between the *virus* and the *disease* it causes. The two things are by no means synonymous, because the same virus may produce entirely different diseases, according to the species of host in the case of plant viruses, and the particular type of tissues invaded with some animal viruses.

This confusion of mind in the early days was not confined to the layman but was also manifest in the attitude of some virus workers. This was mainly due to the difficulty of conceiving the virus as a separate entity since at the time all its known properties were negative ones. Viruses could not be seen, they could not be grown on artificial culture media, they could not be held back by bacteria-proof filter candles and so on. In consequence practically the whole attention was focused on the symptoms. With the modern improvements in technique and the invention of the electron microscope all this has been changed and, as we shall see in the next chapter, the invisible enemy has been made visible.

It was largely because of the purely biological outlook of the early virus workers, who insisted on regarding a virus merely as an unusually small organism, probably a small bacterium, that the isolation of viruses was so long delayed. It was not until the subject was approached from the chemical standpoint, and methods of isolation, such as are used for preparing chemical substances, were employed, that the first plant virus was isolated in a comparatively pure form.

Actually, the first more or less successful attempt to purify and concentrate a virus was made with a bacterial virus, using a centrifuge to spin it out of solution, but this virus was one of the larger ones and did, in fact, have more resemblance to small bacteria. When it is desired to get a pure culture of, say, a pathological bacterium, it can frequently be achieved by " plating out " a small quantity of the organism on a culture medium and allowing it to grow on the surface of the medium. But this cannot be done with any viruses since one of their fundamental characteristics is that they will only multiply inside a living susceptible cell. The separation of the viruses from the hosts' tissues must therefore be done mechanically, and it is here that difficulties arise. There are two main methods of isolating viruses, one, by chemical precipitation, or " salting out "; the other by sedimenting out the virus from solution by high-speed centrifugation. Owing to their comparatively large size as compared with molecules many viruses will sediment to the bottom of a tube in a centrifugal field in a reasonable time and form a compact pellet which remains when the upper, or supernatant, fluid is decanted off.

It is not possible to purify or concentrate some viruses, at all events with the methods at present in use, and this applies particularly to many of those affecting plants. There are two main qualities which are more or less essential in a virus if it is to be purified. It must be stable, that is, it must be able to stand up to the rather harsh chemical treatment, necessary during the purification processes, without becoming denatured, insoluble, or losing its infectivity. Stability is not quite so essential in cases of purification by means of the centrifuge where the treatment is less drastic, but some stability is necessary. The second quality necessary for purification is high concentration of virus in the host, and this is often lacking. In plants, severity of symptoms is no criterion of the amount of virus present, and in many severe virus diseases of plants very little virus can be found. Another important property which is desirable for purification of a plant virus, is that it should be mechanically transmissible by sap-inoculation; we have seen in Chapter 2 that plant viruses vary greatly in their mode of spread, and it is little use if, having attempted to purify the virus, there is no means of testing the virus content of the purified material.

Several years before the first plant virus, that of tobacco mosaic, was isolated in a more or less pure condition, two American workers, Takahashi and Rawlings (1933), suggested that this virus consisted of rod-shaped particles, a suggestion which was later amply confirmed by other methods (see Chap. 10, p. 102).

Minute rods, discs, or leaf-shaped particles which are contained in a flowing liquid tend to become orientated with their long axis parallel to the direction of flow, rather like logs in a stream.   Under these conditions, a liquid containing rods is doubly refractive when the direction of transmission of the incident light is perpendicular to the direction of flow.   This is called " anisotropy of flow " and may be seen in polarised light. When Takahashi and Rawlins suggested that the tobacco mosaic virus particle was rod-shaped it was because they had observed this phenomenon in sap from infected tobacco plants when they squirted it through a narrow tube and watched the flow through a polarising microscope.

As we have already mentioned, the virus of tobacco mosaic was the first plant virus to be isolated in a more or less pure condition.   This was done by Stanley, an American biochemist, and he used chemical methods of salting out previously used in the purification of enzymes.

The simplest method of isolating this virus is to take infected tobacco or tomato plants, mince them and squeeze out the sap, which contains 1-2 gm./litre of virus and much plant material. The latter may be removed by heating the sap to 55° C., which has little effect on the virus.   This may then be precipitated as needles by the addition of salts such as ammonium sulphate or alternatively it may be deposited from the solution as a jelly by centrifuging at 20,000 r.p.m. for an hour.   A few repetitions of either procedure will suffice to give reasonably clear solutions of virus, which will then remain infectious for many years.

If the virus concentration of the final preparation is not less than about four per cent, the solution exhibits the curious property of " layering." After standing for some time, the liquid separates into two layers; these two layers have different solid contents and different appearances, whether viewed by ordinary or polarised light. The upper layer, which is the more dilute, is slightly opalescent by transmitted light and behaves like a suspension of rods or plates which can be orientated by streaming. The lower layer is spontaneously birefringent; it may be perfectly clear by transmitted light, but by reflected light it has a strong sheen. This lower layer can be diluted with water and, after standing, will again separate into two layers. This rather curious layering phenomenon occurs when the concentration of the virus is too great to allow free movement of the particles, which arrange themselves into small boat-shaped drops called " micro-tactoids." These are of slightly higher density and so fall to the bottom, thus producing the lower layer.

By the addition of ten per cent acetic acid or one-third saturation with ammonium sulphate, the virus is precipitated in the form of fine needles or paracrystals. As the particles of tobacco mosaic virus are long rods and not spheres, they do not form true 3-dimensional crystals *in vitro*, but there is considerable evidence that they do so in infected plants.

A virus attacking the cucumber plant, on which it causes a rather characteristic type of mottling, has been shown to have characteristics in common with the tobacco mosaic virus. This was done by means of the serological reactions of the virus, and it is interesting because, as it happens, the relationship could not be shown by any kind of cross-immunity studies in plants, since the cucumber virus is confined to plants of the Cucurbitaceae, which the tobacco mosaic virus will not infect systemically. Incidentally, it may be mentioned that this virus and its strains, known as cucumber viruses 3 and 4, were considered to be, some thirty years ago, the common cucumber mosaic virus attacking cucumber plants in the Lea Valley and elsewhere. Now, however, it has virtually disappeared and its place has been taken by another cucumber mosaic virus of entirely different properties and characteristics, but superficially resembling it. This is an aphid-borne virus and it has been discussed in Chapter 4, dealing with viruses in garden plants.

In order to obtain material of cucumber viruses 3 and 4 for experimental work, it has been necessary to acquire some from a virus laboratory in the U.S.A., where it was originally sent from this country. These viruses can be purified by methods like those used for the purification of tobacco mosaic virus, and when isolated they exhibit properties very similar to those of tobacco mosaic virus. That is to say, solutions of cucumber viruses 3 and 4 show anisotropy of flow and, upon standing, separate into two layers, the lower of which is liquid crystalline, etc., etc.

Another virus which has rod-shaped particles and rather similar properties is potato virus X, and this virus has been dealt with already from the grower's point of view in Chapter 5. By precipitation methods, using ammonium sulphate, Bawden and Pirie (1938a) obtained a colourless solution which separated, on standing, into two layers in the same manner as was described for tobacco mosaic virus. Another plant virus which appears to have rod-shaped particles, this time insect-borne in contrast to the other three viruses, is potato virus Y. This virus, however, is present in the plant in very low concentration and its purification is a matter of some difficulty.

The first plant virus with spherical particles to be purified in a true 3-dimensional crystalline form was that of tomato bushy stunt (Bawden and Pirie, 1938b). By chemical methods of precipitation, using ammonium sulphate and alcohol, a clear colourless preparation can be obtained. If left to stand in solution at 0° C., under correct conditions of salt concentration, etc., crystallisation will begin in a few hours and many crystals will form on the sides of the tube. The crystals are dodecahedra and are shown in Plate IV, p. 53. By using other methods it is possible to produce crystals of a different shape, such as eight-sided prisms.

Perhaps the plant virus most easily purified and crystallised is that of turnip yellow mosaic. Plants infected with the virus are minced and the sap is expressed. The sap is clarified by adding slowly, with stirring, 300 ml. of 90 per cent ethyl alcohol. This produces a copious precipitate which is centrifuged off at once at a low speed. To the supernatant fluid is added a volume of saturated ammonium sulphate equal to half the volume of the clarified sap and the solution is allowed to stand overnight. After a few hours, large numbers of small octahedral crystals are to be found in the liquid and these increase in size with time (Plate V, p. 68). When crystallised out of alcohol instead of ammonium sulphate the virus of turnip yellow mosaic has a different crystalline form. These crystals tend to be birefringent needles, which are deposited in hedgehog-like clumps, but on occasion nearly circular laminae have been observed (Markham and Smith, 1949).

Not counting viruses of the tobacco mosaic type, potato virus X, and other viruses which, owing to their rod-like shape, do not form true 3-dimensional crystals, four plant viruses have been crystallised. These are the viruses of tomato bushy stunt (Plate IV, p. 53), tobacco necrosis (Plate VI, p. 69), southern bean mosaic and turnip yellow mosaic (Plate V, p. 68). Strictly speaking, the tobacco necrosis virus is not a single entity but is a group of biologically similar viruses; in this context it is treated as one virus although all members of the group do not crystallise similarly.

So far only plant viruses have been obtained in a crystalline form; this may be partly because many of the animal viruses have particles which are too large to crystallise and partly because of the difficulty of obtaining sufficient quantities of virus.

For the purification of insect viruses such as those causing the polyhedral diseases described in Chapter 7, the first step in the procedure is to collect a large quantity of the dead infected caterpillars. They are then placed in a glass vessel, preferably tall and narrow, with water and saline, and allowed to decompose. Alternatively the caterpillars can be ground in a mortar and the material lightly washed through fine muslin. In either case they should be left to stand in a tall vessel for some weeks while the polyhedral bodies sediment out to the bottom. Next the supernatant fluid containing the caterpillar debris is carefully decanted, leaving the polyhedral bodies which contain the virus at the bottom of the vessel. These are then washed thoroughly and drawn through a piece of fine muslin with a suction pump. If properly washed, the polyhedra should be white. The next step is to free the virus by dissolving the polyhedra at an alkaline pH of 9 or 10. The dry polyhedra are put into a clean flask and the alkali is added at the rate of 7 ml. of a mixture of 0·008% sodium carbonate and 0·05% sodium chloride for 35 mg. of dry polyhedra. This is left to stand with the vessel closed for two to three hours; when the solution is fairly, but not too, clear, it is spun on the centrifuge at 6,000 r.p. for about five minutes, to sediment the undissolved material. The supernatant fluid which contains the virus is carefully decanted and then centrifuged for one hour at 10,000 r.p.m. This throws down the virus as a bluish white precipitate; after the supernatant liquid has been decanted the precipitate is dissolved in glass-distilled water. After repeating this process, a final solution is given which is opalescent. This is the purified virus which will not, of course, crystallise because of the comparatively large size of the particles (Bergold, 1947).

The worker on viruses affecting the larger animals is handicapped in comparison with the plant virus worker by the difficulty of getting sufficient quantities of virus. In some cases of course this is easier than in others, and virus can be collected and stored until a sufficient quantity has been obtained. For example, with the Shope rabbit papilloma, the warts can be removed from the infected rabbit, covered with glycerol and stored at a temperature of 2-8° C. When enough material has been accumulated the warts are pulped and the virus, after some preliminary treatment, can be sedimented by ultracentrifugation. In one such experiment 50·4 mg. of virus were obtained, a yield of 0·33 mg. of virus from 1 g. of warts.

The difficulty of obtaining enough virus can also be partly solved by growing the virus artificially. For example, influenza virus can be propagated, like many other animal viruses, on the chorio-allantoic membrane of the developing hen's egg. The infectious allantoic fluid is collected and centrifuged at a high speed, 24,000 r.p.m. for two hours. At the end of that time, according to the American workers, the pellet contained 97 per cent of the virus activity.

Historically bacteriophages, or bacterial viruses, as they are now called, are of some interest as they were the first viruses to be isolated in a relatively pure state. This was done by Schlesinger in Germany in the early 1930s. He worked on one of the larger 'phages (now known as T_2) which attack *Escherichia coli*. The methods of isolation used to-day differ only slightly from his methods, and mainly in that nowadays high-speed centrifuges of large capacity are relatively common. To purify the T bacteriophages of *E. coli*, a culture in active growth in broth is inoculated with a dose of 'phage sufficient to infect, say 1/500 of the bacteria. The culture is then diluted with nutrient broth and incubated at 37° with vigorous aeration. The infected cells lyse and each liberates some hundred or more 'phage particles, which in turn infect more bacteria until the medium contains a very large number of virus particles. Resistant bacteria and debris are removed by centrifuging at low speed and the 'phage particles then deposited by a high-speed spin. For very large quantities a milk separator type of centrifuge may be used, and several milligrammes of virus may be isolated. As one milligramme may contain about 2×10^{12} particles, it will be appreciated that the product is very active indeed. Further purification involves a repetition of the low-speed and high-speed spins, and the final preparation is a milky white liquid in which the 'phage particles may be seen under dark ground illumination dancing around. As they are quite small they move fairly rapidly, spinning round as they go, their tails sweeping out arcs in the liquid until they eventually touch a bacterium. This swimming action is, of course, due to the molecular bombardment, or Brownian movement, which goes on in the liquid and is not an active process.

References

BAWDEN, F. C., and PIRIE, N. W. (1938a). Liquid crystalline pre
    parations of potato virus X. *Brit. J. Exp. Path. 19*: 66-82.
BAWDEN, F. C., and PIRIE, N. W. (1938b). Crystalline preparation
    of tomato bushy stunt virus. *Brit. J. Exp. Path. 19*: 251-63.

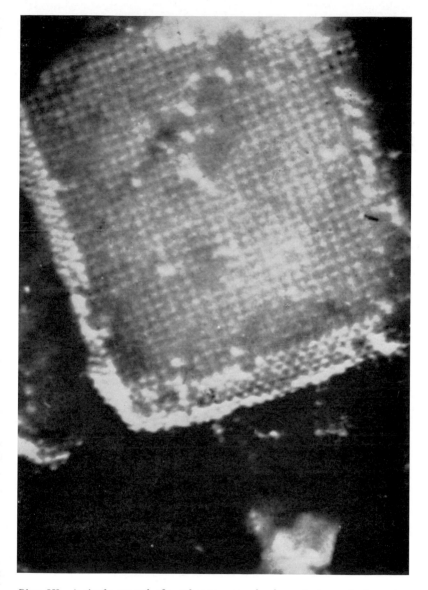

Plate IX. A single crystal of a tobacco necrosis virus photographed on the electron microscope: note the regular arrangement of the virus particles on the face of the crystal. X *c.* 40,000. (*Markham, Smith & Wyckoff*, NATURE *159, 1947*)

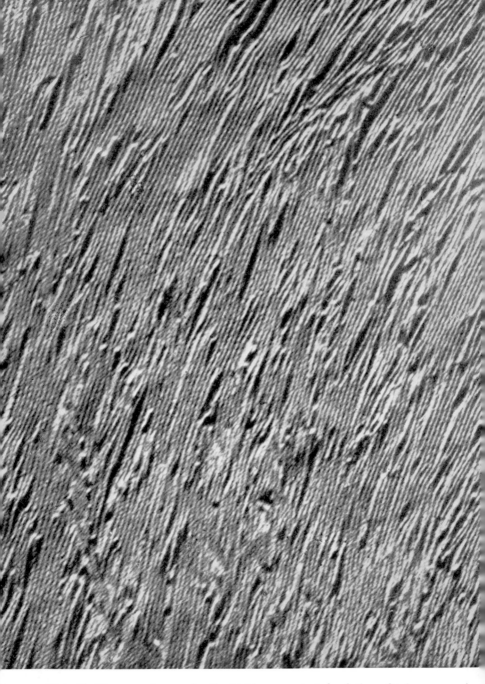

Plate X. Electron micrograph of a highly concentrated solution of tobacco mosaic virus: the rod-shaped particles are so numerous as to form a felt. X 61,000 (*Wyckoff*)

BERGOLD, G. (1947). Die Isolierung des Polyeder-Virus und die Natur der Polyeder. *Z. f. Naturforsch.* *Bd. 2b. Heft 3/4:* 122-43.

MARKHAM, R., and SMITH, KENNETH M. (1949). Studies on the virus of turnip yellow mosaic. *Parasitology,* *39:* 330-42.

TAKAHASHI, W. N., and RAWLINS, T. E. (1933). Rod-shaped particles in tobacco mosaic virus demonstrated by stream double refraction. *Science (N.S.),* *77:* 26.

CHAPTER 10

WHAT VIRUSES LOOK LIKE:
THEIR SIZE AND SHAPE

In an earlier chapter we stated that many of the properties of viruses were of a negative character, one of them being their invisibility because of their minute size. Now, however, with the development of the electron microscope, we are able to see and photograph even the smallest viruses.

The unit of measurement of particles of molecular size is the *millimicron*, written m μ for short, one millionth of a millimetre, and as the limit of resolution with the optical microscope in visible light is about 200 m μ, an object must be at least 250 m μ in diameter to be properly resolved. Now as many of the plant viruses are between 20-30 m μ in diameter, it is obvious that these are far below the limit of resolution with the ordinary microscope. Similarly with ultra-violet light, the wavelength used is about 250 m μ, so that only the larger viruses of 100 m μ and above can be *resolved* by this means, although they can be seen as bright particles with the ordinary microscope using dark ground illumination. In order to resolve the very small plant and animal viruses, therefore, a radiation with a wavelength much shorter than light must be used.

In the electron microscope the illuminating radiation consists of a swiftly moving beam of electrons which corresponds to the beam of light in the optical microscope.

Because glass is opaque to the electron beam, it cannot be used for lenses, so that electric or magnetic " lenses " are used instead to focus the electrons as in a television set. It is necessary also for the electron optical paths to be in a vacuum since gas molecules would scatter the electrons; and the specimen must be dry. The specimen to be photographed is mounted on an exceedingly thin film of collodion supported on a fine metal grid.

The highly magnified image of the specimen may be viewed directly on a fluorescent screen or photographed by means of a plate sensitive to electrons. We have to remember, however, that the specimen must be dry, and as we know that most viruses contain water, this may lead to a certain amount of error in computing size and shape.

The technique of electron micrography has been greatly improved by means of metal shadow casting. Briefly, this consists of coating the specimen with a semi-transparent layer of metal which is deposited obliquely by evaporation in a vacuum. Various metals can be used, particularly, gold, chromium, nickel and uranium, but gold, frequently combined with palladium, seems to be most suitable for small particles. This metal shadow casting gives a three-dimensional effect to the image so that the heights or thicknesses of objects can be estimated from the lengths of the shadows they cast. From this technique much information has been obtained on the morphology of virus particles. In Plates X-XII (pp. 101, 116-17) will be seen some electron micrographs of different virus particles.

Let us now examine some of the results obtained by studying viruses with the electron microscope and see something of their appearance. We shall note in considering the viruses as a whole that there is a remarkable variation in size and shape.

The forecast, made a good many years ago now by Takahashi and Rawlins (1933), that the virus of tobacco mosaic consisted of elongated particles has been amply confirmed by the electron microscope. Not only was this the first virus to be photographed, but it has been photographed more often than any other plant virus and, possibly, any other virus. As will be seen from the picture in Plate X (p. 101), the particles consist of rods of different lengths, the most common being 280×15 mμ, and it is with this size that infectivity seems to be associated. Much smaller particles do occur but it is doubtful if they are infectious.

The rods seem to be fairly rigid and aggregate end to end,

and side to side, so that the actual size of individual particles is obscured.

Quite a number of plant viruses have now been shown to have rod-shaped particles. The two cucumber mosaic viruses, known as cucumber viruses 3 and 4, which are related to the tobacco mosaic group of viruses, have particles which resemble them in size and shape.

Potato virus X, which we have discussed in Chapter 5, also consists of rod-shaped particles, but they lack rigidity and tend to curl and form tangles like pieces of thin string.

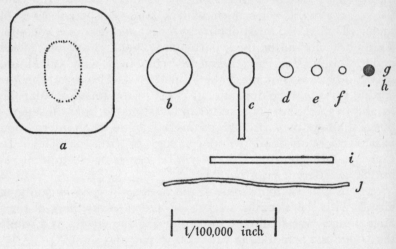

Fig. 2

The sizes of some viruses and proteins compared.
a vaccinia virus, *b* influenza virus, *c* T₂ bacteriophage, *d* tomato bushy stunt virus, *e* turnip yellow mosaic virus, *f* stipple streak virus, *g* *Helix* haemocyanin, *h* cytochrome, *i* tobacco mosaic virus, *j* potato virus X

There is also a good deal of evidence that another potato virus, that of paracrinkle, has rod-shaped particles which, however, appear to be considerably shorter than those of potato virus X (Bawden, Kassanis and Nixon, 1950).

Recent work in America on the viruses attacking cruciferous plants, the cabbage black ringspot virus, for example, which we have already dealt with in Chapter 4, suggests that some of these have particles consisting of long flexuous rods. In a paper recently published Bawden and Nixon (1951) have demonstrated that some other plant viruses are rod-shaped.

There is one plant virus which appears to be much larger than the others we have mentioned if the preliminary work on it is confirmed. This is a potato virus occurring in the U.S.A. known as potato yellow dwarf. Electron micrographs of infected sap show the presence of numerous rods, 200 mμ long and 50 mμ wide, which are not present in the sap of healthy potato plants (Black, Mosley and Wyckoff, 1948).

It must not be supposed from this that all plant viruses have elongated particles: on the contrary, quite a number are spherical or nearly spherical and some of these are very small. About the smallest in the dry state is one of the tobacco necrosis viruses which measures 15 mμ in diameter. The next larger is probably turnip yellow mosaic virus, which has a particle size of about 20 mμ; then comes southern bean mosaic virus and some of the other tobacco necrosis viruses with a diameter of 25 mμ, tomato bushy stunt virus slightly larger with 26 mμ, and squash mosaic virus measuring about 30 mμ.

Examination with the electron microscope of the viruses attacking insects is of much more recent development, and in consequence, much less work has been done. Nevertheless, some very interesting facts have been discovered, although perhaps more problems have been raised than have been solved. As we pointed out in Chapter 7, there are several different types of insect virus diseases, and the commonest—and those most studied—are the so-called polyhedral diseases in which the blood of the infected caterpillar is filled with large numbers of many-sided crystals. When these crystals are dissolved in weak sodium carbonate, the virus contained in them is released and can be photographed. In the polyhedral diseases affecting larvae of the scarlet tiger moth (*Panaxia dominula*) and the currant moth (*Abraxas grossulariata*), the virus particles are rather thick rods measuring about 300 mμ x 40 mμ. These are illustrated in Plate XIII (p. 120) and it will be observed that the polyhedral body is enclosed in a membrane which remains behind when the protein crystal is dissolved. In Plate XIIIa some much larger and fatter rods are visible under the membrane, and these consist, apparently, of bundles of the thinner rods in parallel array, some of which have become separated and lie scattered around. Now one of the problems to be solved is to know what is the significance of the large fat rods which seem, in some cases, though apparently not in all, to consist of bundles of thinner rods. Is this a process of multiplication in which the fat rods break down into the thinner rods? And if so, how do they get inside the crystal? It is significant that, up to the present, careful search with the electron microscope has failed to reveal any of these fat rods in the blood or tissues *outside* the polyhedral bodies. We know, however, that the blood is infective. On the other hand, it is difficult to imagine that multiplication, or at least division, of the rods takes place actually inside the crystal.

Thin rods, which are evidently the elementary particles of the virus, have been demonstrated inside the polyhedra of a number of different caterpillars infected with this type of virus disease, such as the silkworm (*Bombyx mori*), the gipsy moth (*Lymantria monacha*), the alfalfa caterpillar (*Colias* sp.), the currant moth (*Abraxas grossulariata*) and the scarlet tiger moth (*Panaxia dominula*). On the other hand, in some polyhedral diseases these virus rods have not been demonstrated. For example, when the polyhedra from infected caterpillars of the garden tiger (*Arctia caja*) and the cream spot tiger (*A. villica*) are treated with dilute sodium carbonate the result is quite different, and instead of the polyhedral bodies dissolving away and leaving a membrane behind there remains a hollow shell pitted with large numbers of holes of very uniform diameter (Plate XIV, p. 121). There appears to be no enveloping membrane and no rods have been observed. On the other hand, there do sometimes occur clusters of spherical bodies which may be the elementary particles of the virus. It seems, therefore, as if there were at least two different kinds of polyhedral diseases (Smith and Wyckoff, 1950).

There is another type of virus disease attacking insects, such as the caterpillar of the white butterfly and cutworms, which has been studied with the electron microscope (Bergold, 1948). This is known as a capsular disease or " granulosis," and instead of polyhedra there are large numbers of characteristic granules in the infected cells. Under the electron microscope these granules are seen to be capsules, measuring about 230 x 360 millimicrons, which contain the virus. The capsules do not dissolve with weak alkali as do the polyhedra, but with stronger alkali they dissolve to a sufficient extent to liberate the virus, which slips out, leaving behind a rod-shaped cavity. There appears to be only one virus rod or double-rod in each capsule.

We come now to consider the appearance of some of the larger viruses attacking animals, and one, which was the first animal virus to be photographed, is vaccinia virus. This virus has frequently been observed under the optical microscope with dark ground illumination and had, from those observations, been assumed to have a spherical form. When photographed by means of the electron microscope, however, the virus, in the dry state, is brick-shaped with rounded corners (Plate XI, p. 116) and even seems to have a certain amount of structure. The virus particles are enclosed within a membrane and show a characteristic central dense body. The fact that this structure is actually enclosed in a membrane can be demonstrated by treating the virus particles with salt solution and pepsin, which dissolves the contents, leaving the membrane behind.

Another of the larger animal viruses which has been much photographed is that of influenza, and it appears to occur in two distinct forms. One is a spherical form with a diameter of about 100 mμ, the other is an elongated, filamentous form of about the same diameter as the spheres and sometimes itself terminating in a sphere (Plate XII, p. 117). Occasionally also the filaments have the appearance of being segmented into a chain of spheres. This, of course, suggests the possibility of some propagation process, but more evidence is required on this point before a definite opinion can be given.

Several attempts have been made to see virus particles inside tumours. For example, sections through the Rous chicken sarcoma have been photographed and spherical particles measuring from 60-80 mμ have been observed within the cells; the particles have not been observed in sections of normal tissues. It is tempting to assume that these are the sarcoma virus particles and so they may be, but here again further work is required on this aspect of virus study.

Examination of the bacterial viruses, or bacteriophages as they used to be called, revealed the interesting fact that, in the case of the larger ones, for example, T_2 of *Escherichia coli*, the elementary particles were sperm- or tadpole-shaped with a " head " and a " tail." The " heads " may be rounded or egg-shaped or somewhat rectangular, measuring from 60-80 mμ in diameter, the " tails " are relatively short and thick and measure about 120 mμ in length. There appears to be a membrane surrounding the " head " because some chemical treatments or irradiations cause the contents to slip out of the " head " and the membrane or " ghost," with the tails often still attached, remains behind. Stereoscopic electron micrographs of preparations of bacteria infected with virus, made by Dr. T. F. Anderson in the U.S.A., have shown that the virus particles stick into the bacterium tail first, with the result that an infected bacterium looks rather like a pin-cushion.

An electron micrograph of a bacterial virus is shown in Plate VIII, p. 85.

Before we close this short account of the electron microscopy of viruses, reference must be made to some studies made of viruses in their crystalline form. Photographs of single crystals, particularly of one of the tobacco necrosis viruses, reveal the remarkably perfect arrangement of the elementary virus particles, and demonstrate the geometrical regularity of the fine structure of crystals, a regularity which had been inferred from their external symmetry and, for example, by X-ray diffraction. The photograph in Plate IX (p. 100) was taken by Dr. Wyckoff, who describes the preparations as follows. Suspensions of the microcrystals were made in half-saturated ammonium sulphate and spread and dried on a glass slide. They were then shadowed with gold or palladium, stripped from the glass after a collodion coating, and finally strengthened with a very thin layer of vertically applied beryllium. The large square faces on the top of the crystal have their molecules in the form of a square net. The arrangement on the side faces is more difficult to determine but seems to be a hexagonal close-packed net. It is not possible with present methods to photograph all plant virus crystals in this way. Attempts to photograph single crystals of the turnip yellow mosaic virus (see Plate V, p. 68) have failed because the crystals collapsed during the specimen preparations. The spot occupied by the crystal when photographed revealed only an irregular pile of virus particles. This is probably because the crystals contain a considerable amount of water and have a somewhat spongy structure, the virus particles only touching each other over four small areas on their surfaces. Other techniques have in fact shown a structure of the type expected from other data.

References

BAWDEN, F. C., KASSANIS, B., and NIXON, H. L. (1950). The mechanical transmission and some properties of potato para-crinkle virus. *J. Gen. Microbiol.* *4*: 210.

BAWDEN, F. C., and NIXON, H. L. (1951). The application of electron microscopy to the study of plant viruses in unpurified plant extracts. *J. Gen. Microbiol.* *5*: 104-09.

BERGOLD, G. (1948). Über die Kapselviruskrankheit. *Z. Naturforsch.* *3b*: 338-42.

BLACK, L. M., MOSLEY, V. M., and WYCKOFF, R. W. G. (1948). Electron micrography of potato yellow dwarf virus. *Biochim. Biophys. Acta* *2*: 121-23.

SMITH, KENNETH M., and WYCKOFF, R. W. G. (1950). Structure within polyhedra associated with insect virus diseases. *Nature, London, 166*: 861.

TAKAHASHI, W. N., and RAWLINS, T. E. (1933). Rod-shaped particles in tobacco mosaic virus demonstrated by stream double refraction. *Science (N.S.), 77*: 26.

CHAPTER II

CONTROLLING VIRUS DISEASES

IN CONSIDERING the various methods which are now in use for controlling or reducing the effects of the many different types of virus diseases we have thought it better not to separate the diseases of animals and plants into categories but to discuss them together according to the control methods, which we have arranged under five headings.

In spite of the large amount of work which has been, and is still being, done there is perhaps less progress in the control of virus diseases than of diseases caused by other agents. This is especially true in the use of antibiotics.

CONFERRING IMMUNITY ON AN ORGANISM

This method of control is much more applicable to the viruses affecting the higher animals since its efficacy depends upon the production of antibodies which are not, so far as we know, produced in plants. There is, however, one method of conferring a type of immunity on plants to which we shall refer later.

So far as animals, especially man, are concerned, immunity against certain virus diseases can be conferred by inoculation or " vaccination " as it is usually called.

Vaccination can be carried out as follows:

(a) With active virus, (b) with modified virus, (c) with inactivated virus, (d) with antiserum from a recovered animal, (e) with both active virus and antiserum, and (f) with active and inactive viruses combined.

In all these methods, the objective is to call forth in the

vaccinated person or animal, the antibodies or immune bodies which confer protection against a particular disease without producing any serious ill-effects.

Obviously, if vaccination is carried out with active unchanged virus, a serious and unchanged disease will result, except in certain cases where the virus is introduced into the body by an unnatural or non-infective route. For example, influenza is a respiratory disease which normally enters the body by the nose or mouth, but if the virus is inoculated under the skin into ferrets or mice, two susceptible animals, a considerable degree of resistance to subsequent infection is conferred without the development of any illness. Depending upon this, some American workers have practised human vaccination with influenza virus given subcutaneously. Some success in this method has also been obtained with viruses affecting fowls and another affecting sheep and goats.

By far the greatest success has been obtained, however, by the use of modified viruses. The classical examples of this type of vaccination are first, of course, that practised by Jenner a hundred years before the discovery of the first virus. He showed that inoculation with cow-pox, or vaccinia virus, gave complete protection against the more severe form of the disease, smallpox. Secondly, Pasteur, by using a modified or attenuated form of virus, was able to induce immunity to the dreadful disease of rabies.

The methods by which viruses can be modified are of considerable interest. There are two main methods: (1) By growing the virus in animals which are not the natural hosts, and also by using unusual tissues in which to propagate the virus; (2) by culturing the virus on the chorioallantoic membrane of the developing hen's egg.

Dr. Theiler, who has recently been awarded the Nobel Prize for his work on yellow fever, discovered that this virus could be modified by progressive inoculation through mouse brains. Further modification could be brought about by growing the virus in chick embryo tissue. Finally, a strain of yellow fever virus was obtained which could safely be used for vaccination and many millions of doses of this vaccine have now been distributed.

Another case of modification of a virus by propagation in an unnatural host is that of dengue or " break-bone " fever. This was achieved only after much effort and many disappointments because of the great difficulty in finding a suitable animal. Finally a particular strain of white mice was found in which the virus would propagate, and after many serial transfers from mouse to mouse a strain of virus was evolved which gave rise only to the skin rash characteristic of the disease but without the more serious fever and " break-bone " pains. This strain was effective, however, in stimulating the formation of antibodies against the severe form of the disease as well.

Great hopes have been raised that vaccines may be prepared against other virus diseases by the discovery that many viruses can be grown on a membrane inside the developing hen's egg, and this is particularly true of the influenza virus. In 1936 an Australian scientist, Burnet, found that a strain of this virus which had been propagated in ferrets would grow on the egg membrane but gave no sign of injury to the chick embryo. With continued cultivation on eggs, however, the virus gradually became more virulent to the chick embryo and, parallel with this increase in virulence to the chick, there developed a decrease in virulence to man. There are thus hopes that one day a vaccine may be developed which will be efficacious against the annual plague of influenza. There is, however, at least one major difficulty which should be mentioned. Influenza virus occurs in two well-defined strains, known as A and B, neither of which confers immunity against the other. To be of practical use, therefore, any influenza vaccine must be a mixture of both strains of the virus.

Not very much success has been achieved by the use of vaccines prepared from inactivated or " dead " viruses. Formalised virus vaccines have been found fairly satisfactory against dog distemper and equine encephalomyelitis, but phenol is better than formaldehyde for fowl plague. Inactivated rickettsiae have been used for a number of years to prepare a vaccine against Rocky Mountain spotted fever. The vaccine is prepared from the infected ticks which transmit the disease, and is more potent when old infective ticks are used.

A good example of the use of antiserum from a recovered animal is given by some experiments in the treatment of measles. The increasing use of blood transfusion and the storage of blood in " blood banks " led to the discovery that the gamma-globulin fraction of processed human blood might be used as a means of controlling measles. Since so large a proportion of adult human beings are immune to the disease, it was sure to be rich in antibodies.

Since the serum of an animal recovering from a virus disease contains antibodies which are capable of neutralising the virus, it is possible to prepare serum-virus mixtures which are non-infective. Such mixtures have been used to some extent against cattle plague and dog distemper, the procedure being to inoculate first the virus on one side of the animal and to follow this up a little later with an inoculation on the other side with the immune serum.

Finally we have immunity conferred by inoculation with active and inactivated viruses combined. This was practised successfully by two English scientists, Dunkin and Laidlaw, in their pioneer work with dog distemper. Their procedure was first to inoculate the dog with virus which had been inactivated by means of formaldehyde. This initiates a low-grade resistance which allows for the second inoculation of active virus; by this means a solid immunity is achieved.

Before we leave the subject of conferring immunity on an organism we must refer to a kind of acquired immunity to virus diseases in plants. This is, so far as we know, of a fundamentally different nature from the acquired immunity in animals which we have just described, because of the apparent absence of antibody formation in plants. Most plant viruses occur in related strains or biotypes, and it has been discovered (Thung, 1931, Salaman, 1933) that if a plant is already infected with a virus, then such a plant is usually, but not always, immune from attack by another virus, provided that the second virus is a strain of, or

related to, the first virus. There seems to be no limit to infection
with different viruses.

The exact mechanism of this type of immunity is not known,
but it is thought that when the cells of the plant are fully para-
sitised by the first virus, the second virus cannot get a hold. It
seems to be a case of first come, first served. This type of immunity
in plants is largely academic in its application to the control of
plant virus diseases. It is necessary that, of two strains of a virus,
one should produce a very mild disease and this one should be
used to " vaccinate " the plant against the second, more virulent
type. Obviously, no benefit would accrue from inoculating a
plant with a virus which produced a serious disease.

Destroying the Virus in the Tissues of the Host

So far not very much progress has been made with this
method of control, which is still in its infancy. There are two
modes of treatment, the use of chemicals (chemotherapy),
including the use of antibiotics such as penicillin, and, in the
case of plants, heat treatment.

As regards antibiotics, what success has been obtained has
been mainly against the rickettsiae and not the small viruses. Of
two of the more recently discovered antibiotics, *chloromycetin* has
been used successfully against scrub-typhus and certain related
infections. The other, *aureomycin*, which is a metabolic product
of *Streptomyces aureofaciens*, has a marked curative action on viruses
of the psittacosis group and certain rickettsial diseases when
grown on the chorioallantoic membrane of the developing hen's
egg. Aureomycin has also been used successfully on human
patients suffering from Rocky Mountain spotted fever and
" Q " fever.

In plants there seems to be only one record of the apparently
successful treatment of a virus disease by chemotherapy. An
American worker, Stoddard, states that he cured buds from
peach trees affected with X disease by soaking them in water
solutions of quinhydrone, urea and thiosulphate.

Some plant viruses are very susceptible to exposure to heat

and this opens the way to curing virus-diseased plants by growing them at a temperature at which the virus is destroyed. This method, of course, is only applicable to certain viruses, and also only to certain plants, as not all plants will withstand exposure to comparatively high temperatures. Some virus diseases of the peach known as peach yellows, little peach and rosette, have been cured by Kunkel (1936) working in America. That the trees were actually freed of the virus was demonstrated by grafting a piece of a treated tree on to a healthy tree, which induced no disease in the latter. Conversely, the treated trees could be reinfected by grafting them with a piece (scion) of a diseased tree. This demonstrates, incidentally, the lack of any acquired immunity of the kind we have discussed in the animal viruses. Kunkel was the pioneer in this method of curing virus-infected plants and, in addition to the peach viruses, he (1941) showed that certain plants infected with the aster yellows virus, such as the periwinkle, could also be cured by this means. It was not possible, however, to cure the aster plant itself as it could not survive the necessary treatment of being grown at 40° C. for two weeks.

DESTROYING THE INSECT VECTORS OF VIRUSES

The prospects of controlling virus diseases by destroying the insects responsible for their spread are brighter now in consequence of the discovery of the new insecticides, such as D.D.T. and the chemicals which become systemic in plants.

In Naples in 1944, for the first time, an outbreak of typhus fever was stopped completely by reason of the lethal effect of D.D.T. on the louse which transmits the disease. D.D.T. is also very toxic to mosquitoes, and there is now reason to expect progress in the elimination of this important insector vector, especially in view of the developments in aerial distribution of insecticides.

The destruction of the insect vectors of plant viruses has now advanced a step further in virtue of the development of the so-called " systemic insecticides." These are chemicals which are taken up by the plant itself without apparent injury but are lethal to any insect feeding on the plant. One great advantage in the use of this type of insecticide is that it is selective in its action in the sense that only insects actually feeding on the treated plant are killed. This means that the beneficial parasites and predacious insects are left unharmed, and are not destroyed wholesale, as is the case with indiscriminate application of other poisons which kill by contact, such as D.D.T.

Apart from this, attempts to destroy insect vectors of plant viruses have not been very successful, partly because a very few insects can cause a great many infections and partly because the act of spraying or dusting is liable to disperse the insects over a wider area and thus help to disseminate the virus.

Avoiding Infection

In this category may be included such measures as general hygiene, eliminating virus reservoirs and, in the case of plants, avoiding or dodging the insect vector.

Included in general hygiene are the obvious precautions, like isolation and quarantine. In the case of such diseases of man as influenza and the common cold it is hardly necessary to point out the danger of unrestrained sneezing and coughing. There is evidence that the droplets from a sneeze may remain suspended in the air for as long as ten minutes. Added to this is the fact that influenza virus may survive drying under ordinary atmospheric conditions and can be distributed in the air on dust particles.

As regards virus diseases of plants, quarantine regulations which govern the import of plants into the country are at a disadvantage owing to the difficulty of knowing whether a given plant may not be " carrying " a latent virus which can only be discovered by scientific tests not practicable under the circumstances.

Mention of latent viruses brings up the question of virus reservoirs and their elimination. Such reservoirs, or sources, of infection may be of considerable importance, especially as

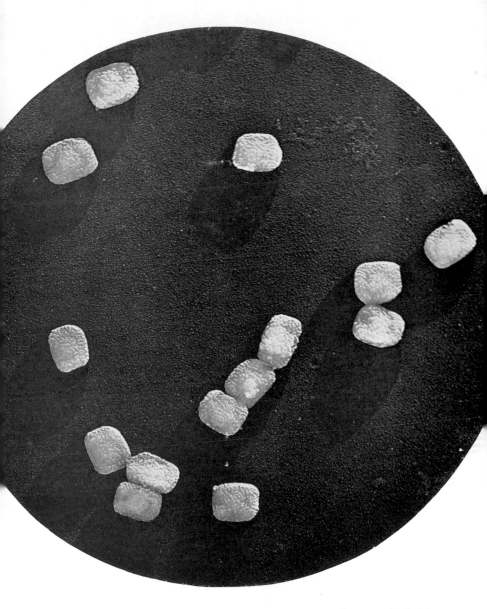

Plate XI. Electron micrograph of vaccinia virus, gold shadowed: note the brick-like appearance of the particles. X 64,500 (*Dawson & McFarlane*, NATURE *161, 464, 1948*)

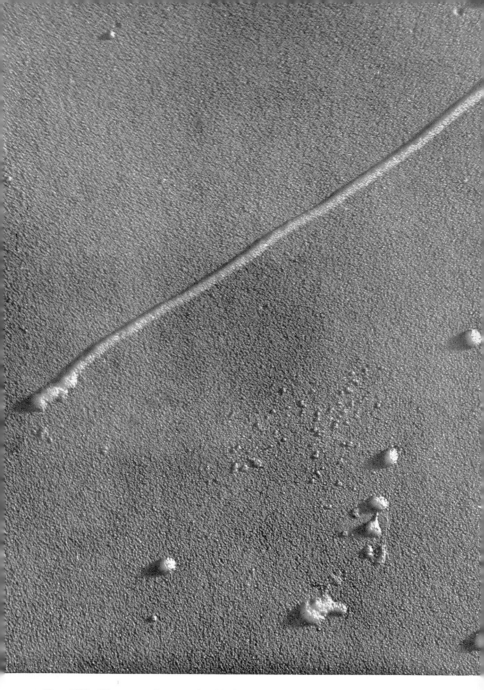

Plate XII. Electron micrograph of influenza virus, Weiss strain. X 37,000 (*Wyckoff*)

regards plant virus diseases. In animals such virus reservoirs are usually some species, other than the one normally affected, which either reacts very slightly to infection or else does not react at all but still retains the virus in its blood. Such animals are known as " carriers." There are three virus diseases of animals to which the problem of carriers is thought to apply. These are African horse sickness, where some species of wild game may act as a carrier, jungle yellow fever in which it is known that many miscellaneous wild animals may harbour the virus in their blood long enough for mosquitoes to pick it up, and the mosquito-borne virus of equine encephalomyelitis. There is some evidence that wild birds may harbour the encephalomyelitis virus, and the egret and the " prairie chicken " have been suspected.

Reservoirs of virus infection for plants may be of several kinds. One of the most important is the existence of wild host plants which may be " carriers " or show only mild symptoms. For example, it has been shown lately that some of the giant forest trees in West Africa carry the virus of " swollen shoot," a disease which has devastated the cocoa plantations of the Gold Coast. Another source of infection is found in " volunteer " plants left over from the previous season's crop. This is especially true of potatoes and of sugar-beets and mangolds, all three of which are usually virus-infected when they persist over the winter. Similarly with the leaf-crinkle disease of cotton, it has been demonstrated that the " ratoon " cotton, those plants left behind after the crop is harvested, are the main source of infection for the next year's crop.

The virus of tobacco mosaic is one of the most infectious and resistant viruses known, and the sources of infection are varied and unexpected. Most commercial brands of cigarettes and tobacco are heavily infected with viable virus and it is an easy matter for a smoker to transfer the virus to the tomato crop. It is only necessary for one or two plants to be infected in this manner; after this, the rest of the plants in the glasshouse become infected from these during the ordinary course of tending the plants.

Each year many tomato growers cannot understand how

their new crop of tomatoes becomes infected with the virus of tobacco mosaic. Apart from the risk of infection by smoking, just mentioned, it is quite easy for the virus to over-winter in dried sap on the staging and wires of the glasshouse. The following experiment illustrates this; two commercial tomato houses were selected, one of which had been sprayed with formalin whilst the other had not. The wiring and staging of the two houses were swabbed down with cotton wool and the two lots of cotton wool were tested for the presence of virus. The cotton wool from the unsprayed house was found to contain active virus but that from the sprayed house was not. Probably the mere fact of spraying was sufficient to remove the virus since weak formalin by itself would not destroy it. Washing down the staging and wires with hot water and soap would be equally, if not more, efficacious, and tomato growers would find that this simple precaution would be well worth while.

Sometimes the insect vectors of important plant viruses can be circumvented by careful selection of the time and place of planting. The large-scale growing of " seed " potatoes in particular areas of Scotland is a good example of avoiding or dodging the insect vector. The peach and potato aphid, *Myzus persicae*, is the most important vector of potato viruses but it does not thrive in the humid atmosphere of the seed-potato areas in Scotland. Similarly certain very hot and dry situations in Africa have been selected for growing " seed " potatoes because again the aphid is unable to thrive under such conditions.

A study of the life-history of the peach and potato aphid shows that it can over-winter in three ways, in heated glasshouses, on brassica crops out of doors in mild winters, and as a winter egg on peach trees. This suggests that there are certain sites where it would be unwise to grow potatoes. In some of the seed-potato areas in Western Germany it has been made compulsory for owners of peach trees to spray their trees to keep down the numbers of aphids.

Miscellaneous Methods of Control

There are two approaches to control which we can appropriately consider under this heading, the breeding of virus-resistant types and the rather drastic method of destruction of the affected organism.

Not much seems to have been achieved in the breeding of virus-resistant animals, and what progress there has been in this direction has been mainly with plants. One of the outstanding successes is the production in the U.S.A. of sugar-beet varieties resistant to the curly-top disease. This has allowed the growing of sugar-beet in areas where it was previously impossible to grow this crop. Similarly with a serious virus disease of cotton in the Sudan known as leaf-crinkle and the mosaic disease of sugar-cane, the production of virus-resistant varieties has greatly reduced the damage done by these diseases.

An interesting example of what a plant-breeder can sometimes do to defeat a virus disease is given by some work on the tobacco plant. A species related to the tobacco plant, *Nicotiana glutinosa*, reacts to infection with tobacco mosaic virus in a characteristic manner. Instead of producing an " overall " or systemic disease, the virus is localised at the point of entry in a spot or lesion without further spread through the plant. The gene responsible for this type of reaction has now been transferred to the tobacco plant and this gives a good hope of control because, with the virus localised in the leaf, infection cannot spread through the crop.

In breeding potatoes for resistance to certain potato virus diseases it is rather paradoxical to find that the tendency is to aim at extreme susceptibility. This is known as " field immunity," and such plants are killed outright by the virus. In consequence the virus itself is also destroyed and so cannot spread.

Perhaps the best examples of control of a virus disease by destruction of the affected host is the method followed in this country for dealing with foot-and-mouth disease of cattle, and to a lesser extent with fowl-pest. This policy of slaughter is ruthlessly applied and rigorously carried out. As soon as an outbreak has been confirmed, all the infected animals and any that may have been in contact with them, are slaughtered and the carcasses burnt. Farm buildings, etc., are disinfected and a standstill order on the movement of cattle into or out of the prohibited area comes into force.

In conclusion, we should like to emphasise that, so far as plants are concerned, much control can be achieved by the application of good farming hygiene, by the use of inspection and field certification schemes, by the isolation, wherever possible, of a healthy susceptible crop from a nearby infected one, and particularly by the choice of healthy virus-free propagating material in the case of crops which are vegetatively propagated.

References

KUNKEL, L. O. (1936). Heat treatments for the cure of yellows and other virus diseases of the peach. *Phytopath.* *26*: 809-30.

KUNKEL, L. O. (1941). Heat cure of aster yellows in periwinkles. *Amer. J. Bot.* *28*: 761-69.

SALAMAN, R. N. (1933). Protective inoculation against a plant virus. *Nature, 131*: 468.

THUNG, T. H. (1931). Smetstoff en plantencel by enkele virusziekten van de Tabaksplant. *Nederland-Indisch Naturw., Handelingen 6de Congres, 1931*: 450-463.

Plate XIIIa. Short fat virus rods remaining within the membranes of polyhedra from the currant moth caterpillar after treatment with sodium carbonate. X 20,000. (*Smith & Wyckoff, 1951 Research*)

    b. Many thin virus rods liberated from the polyhedral body by sodium carbonate treatment. Scarlet tiger caterpillar X 20,500. (*Smith & Wyckoff, 1951 Research*)

a

Plate XIII. Caption opposite

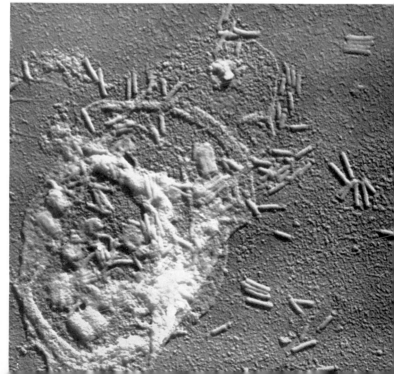

b

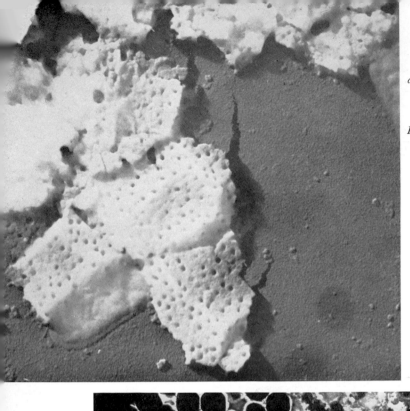

a

Plate XIV. Cap
opposite

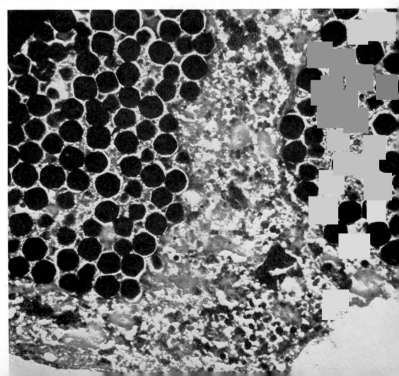

b

CHAPTER 12

THE NATURE OF THE VIRUSES

FOR MANY YEARS, the only certain fact known about the viruses
was that they were exceedingly small, even compared with such
minute organisms as bacteria. There was also no reason for
anyone to have any preconceived ideas about their composition.
Although the obvious way of finding out more about viruses was
to isolate a quantity and study it, the difficulties involved were
sufficient to deter most workers. It is true that a certain amount
was known about the vaccinia virus, which has, of course, been
studied for a long time because of its importance in medicine,
and it was known that suspensions containing this virus also
contained minute dancing granules which were evidently the
same as the " elementary bodies " just visible in microscopic
preparations of infected tissues. These bodies were regarded
merely as very small bacteria. In 1934, however, a German
research worker, M. Schlesinger, who later came to England to
escape Nazi persecution, announced that he had isolated visible
amounts of a bacteriophage by high-speed centrifuging and gave
some details about the chemical composition of his preparations
(Schlesinger, 1934). They contained protein and phosphorus, and
gave reactions for a substance now known as deoxypentose

Plate XIVa. Pitted fragments of polyhedra from infected cream spot tiger
caterpillars after treatments with sodium carbonate X 21,000.
(Smith & Wyckoff, 1951 Research)

b. Great masses of polyhedra in two cells of a section through
a diseased clothes moth caterpillar X 3,000.
(Smith & Wyckoff, 1951 Research)

nucleic acid, which is an invariable component of the nuclei of all cells. Two years later, F. C. Bawden and N. W. Pirie, two young Cambridge research workers, one a plant pathologist and the other a biochemist, noted that their partially purified potato virus X preparations were mainly protein in composition. Shortly afterwards W. M. Stanley, a chemist working in the Rockefeller Institute in America, made the announcement which was later to gain him the Nobel Prize, that he had purified the tobacco mosaic virus and had crystallised it, and that the virus was indeed an ordinary protein. Although it later transpired that his crystals did not have all the properties of true crystals, but were rather " liquid crystals " or paracrystals, this discovery was certainly fundamental to our knowledge of viruses (Stanley, 1936).

It is interesting to note here that, as is so frequent with great scientific discoveries, several people in various parts of the world were all engaged in the same problem and reaching the same conclusions. Apart from the Cambridge workers, R. J. Best (1936) in Australia had also noted that the tobacco mosaic was a protein of the type known as a globulin.

NUCLEOPROTEIN MOLECULES

The second great step in the chemistry of the viruses was made in 1936 by Bawden and Pirie, who found that the tobacco mosaic virus was a nucleoprotein, containing some six per cent of ribonucleic acid combined with 94 per cent of protein, and they showed in collaboration with the X-ray crystallographer, J. D. Bernal (1936), that the virus was composed of rod-shaped particles having a diameter of 6/100,000,000 of an inch. It is interesting to note that this announcement was made more than three years before this virus was first seen under the electron microscope.

VIRUS CRYSTALS

Bawden and Pirie were responsible in the next few years for purifying a number of plant viruses, namely potato virus X, which proved to be a rod rather like tobacco mosaic, cucumber viruses 3 and 4, which were not known to be relations of the tobacco mosaic virus until they had been purified and the similarity of the preparations of the two viruses had been noticed, and tomato bushy stunt, which was the first virus to be crystallised as true crystals. Pirie with K. M. Smith, Spooner and Mac-Clement (1938) was also responsible for the crystallising of the tobacco necrosis virus. All these viruses proved to be nucleo-proteins containing ribonucleic acid. Although the presence of nucleic acid in tobacco mosaic virus was at first denied by the American workers, the truth was so evident that opinion swung to the other extreme, and a belief sprang up that all viruses were nucleoproteins and as such, of necessity, consisted of single molecules.

This was unfortunate and has led to much loose thinking. It is, however, undoubted that many plant viruses are indeed molecules, just as much as are the proteins which comprise haemoglobin, the red colouring matter of our blood, or insulin, the protein from the pancreas which is deficient in people suffering from diabetes.

PROTEINS AND NUCLEIC ACIDS

As many viruses have been shown to contain protein and nucleic acid, it may be profitable at this point to give some idea of the complexity of these substances and of their composition.

Proteins are the essential building blocks of living tissues. They form the muscles, skin, hair and organs, and also constitute the enzymes, and some hormones such as insulin. In fact, it has been said that " Life is the mode of existence of the proteins."

Although they have such a complex series of functions to perform, the proteins are themselves only built up of some twenty fairly simple sub-units known as amino acids, acids containing nitrogen, carbon, hydrogen and oxygen, and all having a similar basic structure. Several amino acids also contain other elements such as sulphur and iodine. Using these twenty-odd amino acids as building blocks, giant molecules are constructed containing hundreds and even thousands of atoms, ranging in size from the protein cytochrome having a molecular weight of only about 10,000, through the various structural proteins and enzymes, to the giant respiratory proteins of the snails and the even larger plant viruses, having molecular weights of millions. All these differ only in the proportions and amounts of the amino acids in their molecules and, sometimes, in the presence of another substance attached to the protein. In the case of the blood's haemoglobin, for example, the red colour and the biological activity is due to *haem*, a nitrogen-containing substance having iron bound to it. In the viruses this extra component is nucleic acid.

The nucleic acids have been known as constituents of organisms since 1871, when a young Swiss physiologist, Friedrich Miescher, discovered a phosphorus-containing substance as the main constituent of animal nuclei. Since then these substances have been found in all cells of every organism, with the exception of certain highly specialised cells which are not capable of division or synthetic ability, such as the red cells of mammalian blood. Like the proteins, the nucleic acids are built up from simple building blocks, the nucleotides, which are organic acids containing phosphoric acid, a sugar, which is either ribose or 2-deoxyribose, and a nitrogen-containing base. The latter is either a purine (a relative of caffein and of uric acid) or a pyrimidine (which is similar chemically to certain sleeping drugs, the barbiturates). Only two purines are known to occur in nucleic acids, adenine and guanine, and only five pyrimidines— uracil, cytosine, thymine, 5-methyl cytosine and 5-hydroxymethyl cytosine—the last of which is only known as a constituent of certain bacteriophages (Wyatt and Cohen, 1952). These giant molecules, the nucleic acids, accordingly have their specificity decided by the arrangement and proportions of the four or five nucleotides which they contain and by the nature of the sugar constituent, rather than by the complexity of the nucleotides themselves.

The nucleic acids fall naturally into two groups, according to the sugar which they contain, and these are known as the ribonucleic acids and the deoxyribonucleic acids respectively.

The former are usually to be found in the cytoplasm of cells and the latter in the nuclei, though cases are now known where this is not so. Originally it was thought that there were only two kinds of nucleic acid, typified by the ribonucleic acid of yeast and by the deoxyribonucleic acid of the thymus gland and of fish sperm, but recent work has shown that a very large number of nucleic acids does exist, the variation being most obvious among the ribonucleic acids, which are now known to be connected in some way with the mechanism of protein synthesis. The deoxyribonucleic acids are almost invariably associated with the nuclei of both animals and plants, and are probably the actual bearers of the hereditary characters of the cells.

THE FUNCTION OF THE CONSTITUENTS OF VIRUSES

The plant viruses which have been studied so far are, as we have said, nucleoprotein molecules, but recent studies suggest that the term molecule in this case includes a physical compound analogous to the " clathrates," compounds having a cage-like exterior enclosing an inert atom without any actual chemical bonds being involved. Those plant viruses about which anything is known would appear to have such a structure, the protein part acting as a protective covering for the nucleic acid and also as a mechanism by which the latter can invade the host cells. The evidence for this comes from a mass of information accumulated over years. For long it has been known that the " vital " part of many viruses is much smaller than the virus itself. This information (Lea and Smith, 1942) has been obtained by bombarding viruses with gamma rays and a particles from radium and with X-rays. These sub-atomic bullets blast any molecule which they hit because their intrinsic energy is much greater than that involved in holding molecules together, and their number may be counted fairly easily. It is then only necessary to put the virus, preferably dry, in position and fire rays at it until, say, half the particles have been rendered non-infectious. Then, knowing the strength of radiation (number of bullets), it is possible to calculate that volume or area of the virus which has to be hit to inactivate it. In this way it has been found that the sensitive part is *invariably* considerably smaller than the virus itself, in the case of tobacco mosaic virus being about 5-6 per cent of the weight of the particle or approximately the weight of the nucleic acid contained in the particle. Again, much time has been devoted to altering the protein part of the molecule by substituting some of its chemical groupings by others, by removing part of the molecule by enzymes or by adding on extra amino acids. These treatments, unless very severe, have no effect on the virus infectivity at all, while the progeny are invariably unaltered.

That the nucleic acid part is very important is also suggested by the fact that we have found that in related strains of viruses the former is of a relatively constant composition, while the variation in composition between the nucleic acids from unrelated viruses is so great that a simple analysis is often enough to differentiate between, say, the tomato bushy stunt, tobacco mosaic and turnip yellow mosaic viruses (Markham and Smith, 1951). In the case of the last-named virus we have very suggestive evidence of the function of the nucleic acid component. In plants infected by this virus two types of particle are found, both superficially alike and having much in common. One type, however, is non-infectious and has no nucleic acid in it, while the other has nucleic acid in it and is infectious. The particles occur in the proportion of one non-infectious particle to two infectious ones, and recent work on other viruses suggests that the non-infectious particles may be the empty shells of the previous generations of virus particles. Although no other plant virus disease is known in which two kinds of particle are produced identical in size and shape, but differing in that one contains nucleic acid and is infectious, while the other does not contain nucleic acid and is not infectious, it now seems likely that this may not be an isolated instance. The tobacco mosaic virus is known to be built up from a large number of small protein sub-units forming a rod, in which these units are arranged in a regular pattern having a spiral form and resembling a crystal on a small scale. Recently it has been found that while no rods devoid of nucleic acid appear to be present in infected plants, there are plenty of the small sub-units which may by chemical treatment be made to crystallise into rods which are non-infectious and contain no nucleic acid. Similar particles may easily occur in the case of other virus infections.

Perhaps the most spectacular evidence, however, has come from work on bacteriophages. Many of these viruses are tadpole-shaped, having quite long tails, and Anderson found that they use these tails as a means for attaching themselves to bacteria. This simple but important fact was only discovered after very special techniques had been developed for the electron microscopy, because if the preparations are allowed to dry the thin tails break off, and so a method was developed for drying the particles by washing them in a liquid which could be turned to a gas instan-taneously without any surface drying down to flatten out the particles. For this purpose Anderson used a liquid gas, liquid carbon dioxide, which suddenly and completely turns from a liquid to a gas at a temperature of $31 \cdot 1°$ C. As this transition takes place at a pressure of more than 73 atmospheres,[1] the drying has to take place inside a " bomb." By this means he managed to preserve the specimens, showing the virus particles sticking on to bacteria by their tails, which are only about one-millionth of an inch thick. Naturally this attachment is very fragile, and by stirring the suspension of infected bacteria it is possible to drag the virus particles off again, the tails being broken in the process. Anderson also found that if bacteriophages were put into strong salt solutions and then into water, the nucleic acid came out, leaving " ghosts ": particles with heads which are apparently hollow. By this and other means it has been shown that the heads of the particles are bags containing nucleic acid. Without their nucleic acid, however, the ghosts readily attack bacteria and kill them, but cannot multiply in the process.

Recently Hershey and Chase (1952) have grown bacteria in media containing radioactive phosphorus and sulphur, and then from these bred radioactive bacteriophage particles. Such

[1] 982 lb./sq. inch.

particles are labelled in their two major components: the nucleic acid by the phosphorus and the protein skin by the sulphur which it contains. Consequently the fate of these constituents can be followed with ease by measurements of radioactivity, which is the most sensitive method known for the detection of substances. By such measurements Hershey and Chase found that within a few minutes of adding their bacteriophage, radio-active phosphorus was to be found inside the bacteria, and if the suspension was then stirred vigorously all the sulphur was to be found in the liquid and none in the bacteria. Apparently what

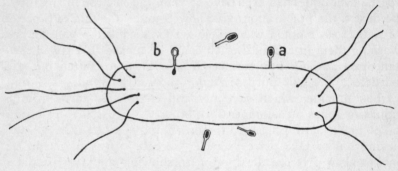

FIG. 3

A diagram of the way in which bacteriophages attack bacteria and infect them. The dark material which they inject through their tails (*a*, *b*) is responsible for the infection and appears to be predominantly deoxyribonucleic acid

happens is this. The bacteriophage particles drift about in the solution until their tails make contact with a bacterium (Fig. 3a). The tail then sticks on firmly and the contents of the head are extruded through the tail, which presumably is hollow, into the bacterium (Fig. 3b). These contents, which consist mainly or entirely of nucleic acid, then go on to monopolise the enzymes of the bacterium in order to make new bacteriophage particles. In this process, which takes about thirty minutes, a new constituent, 5-hydroxymethyl cytosine, has to be synthesised in fairly large amounts, in order to satisfy the needs of the hundred or more daughter virus particles which emerge when the bacterium bursts.

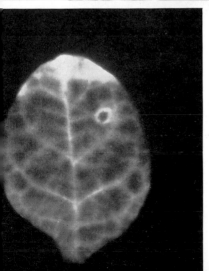

Plate XVa. X-ray photograph of a tobacco plant infected with the " rosette " disease, showing the great distortion of the mid ribs and leaf veins

b. Radioautograph of a leaf of a tobacco plant which was grown in the presence of radioactive phosphorus. This " photograph " was obtained without the use of light, the radioactivity of the leaf causing it to imprint its image on a photographic plate. The leaf was used in an attempt to determine how aphids pick up virus from plants

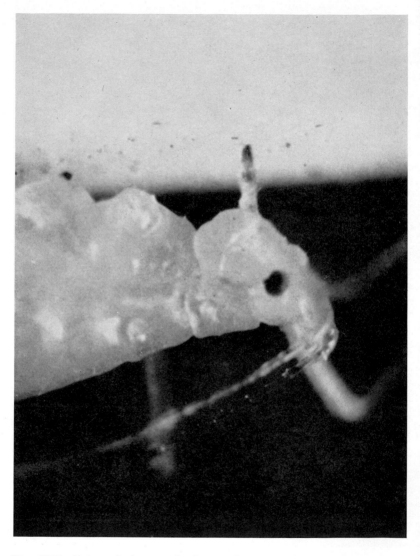

Plate XVI. Enlarged photograph of part of an aphid, *Macrosiphum pisi*, the pea aphid, showing the method of feeding. X 50

Taking this recent evidence into account, one would tend to modify our earlier statement to " Life is the mode of existence of the nucleic acids," the proteins apparently being merely substances produced by them to serve their own ends. In fact, it is extremely difficult in some cases to draw an exact border-line between virus behaviour and the behaviour of nucleic acids. It is now known, for example, that certain kinds of bacteria, one being the diphtheria organism, may be induced to change from a harmless form to a disease-causing form merely by infecting it with a bacteriophage. In this infection a certain number of the bacteria are killed, but some survive and carry the infection indefinitely, and it is those bacteria which survive, which are disease-producing. Now it has been known for some time that a similar change in the pneumonia organism can be effected by nucleic acid obtained from a disease-causing strain, and now such things as resistance to penicillin among the pneumonia organisms have been found to be transmissible to strains susceptible to penicillin by means of nucleic acid isolated from the resistant types. The similarity of such a " transformation " to one caused by bacteriophage infection is clear, the only obvious difference being that in bacteriophage-induced transformation a certain number of bacteria are destroyed, and the rest though being carriers normally do lyse under adverse conditions. It seems certain that research into such subjects will cause us to change our views about the nature and origin of the viruses in the next few years.

The viruses which have been discussed here are of a very simple form, but it must not be thought that all viruses are equally simple. They range from the ribonucleoprotein plant viruses on the one hand, through the polyhedral viruses, which have a more complex structure, but consist only of protein and deoxyribonucleic acid, to bacteriophages which may also contain traces of fat, and have the complex syringe mechanism for infecting their hosts, to the large animal viruses which contain both kinds of nucleic acid, protein, fats and various other components, and which, far from being molecules, seem to resemble small bacteria. It seems quite evident that among the viruses we have a mixed population ranging from degenerate micro-organisms such as vaccinia down to the plant viruses and bacterio-phages, where only the bare essentials for ensuring their multi-plication are to be found. The obvious similarities among the group are most probably due to the necessity in all such viruses to have nucleic acid protected from the external environment by protein until such a time as it is in a position to reduplicate itself.

References

ANDERSON, T. F., RAPPAPORT, C., and MUSCATINE, N. A. (1953). Le Bacteriophage, Institut Pasteur, Paris.

BAWDEN, F. C., and PIRIE, N. W. (1936). Experiments on the Chemical Behaviour of Potato Virus X. *Brit. J. Exp. Path. 17*: 64-74.

BAWDEN, F. C., and PIRIE, N. W. (1938). Crystalline preparations of tomato bushy stunt virus. *Brit. J. Exp. Path. 19*: 251-63.

BAWDEN, F. C., PIRIE, N. W., BERNAL, J. D., and FANKUCHEN, I. (1936). Liquid crystalline substances from virus-infected plants. *Nature, London, 138*: 1051.

BEST, R. J. (1936). Precipitation of the tobacco mosaic virus complex at its isoelectric point. *Austr. J. Exp. Biol. Med. Sci. 14*: 1-13.

HERSHEY, A. D., and CHASE, M. (1952). Independent functions of viral protein and nucleic acid in growth of bacteriophage. *J. Gen. Physiol., 36*: 39.

LEA, D. E., and SMITH, K. M. (1942). The inactivation of plant viruses by radiation. *Parasitology, 34*: 227.

MARKHAM, R., and SMITH, J. D. (1951). Chromatographic studies of nucleic acids 4. The nucleic acid of the turnip yellow mosaic virus, including a note on the nucleic acid of the tomato bushy stunt virus. *Biochem. J. 49*: 401.

PIRIE, N. W., SMITH, K. M., SPOONER, E. C., and MacCLEMENT, W. D. (1938). Purified preparations of tobacco necrosis virus. *Parasitology, 30*: 543-51

SCHLESINGER, M. (1934). Zur frage der chemischen Zusammenset-zung des Bakteriophagen. *Biochem. Z. 273*: 306.

STANLEY, W. M. (1936). The isolation from diseased turkish tobacco plants of a crystalline protein possessing the properties of tobacco mosaic virus. *Phytopathology 26*: 305-20.

WYATT, G. R., and COHEN, S. S. (1952). A new pyrimidine base from bacteriophage nucleic acids. *Nature, London, 170*: 1072.

MIESCHER, F. (1871). In Die histochemischen und physiologischen Arbeiten von Friedrich Miescher, vol. 2, F. C. W. Vogel, Leipzig (1897).

CHAPTER 13

SIMPLE TECHNIQUES

IN THIS CHAPTER we give instruction in some easy methods by means of which any reader who has a glasshouse can carry out for himself one or two simple experiments with plant viruses. The purpose of these experiments is to attempt to demonstrate the existence of a virus in a crop which may not be thriving. Put in another way, the aim is the recognition of a virus which may or may not be causing a visible disease, and it is based on the infectious nature of the virus and its transmission to another plant which reacts in a manner different from the one under investigation.

How to Inoculate Plants

In this case we are using the word "inoculate" in the narrow sense of applying the sap of the suspected plant to the leaves of the test plant. The procedure is simple enough and consists of grinding up a few of the younger leaves of the plant to be tested with a porcelain pestle and mortar, or even between two spoons. The sap thus extracted can be roughly clarified by squeezing the pulp with the finger and allowing the sap to run to one side of the tilted mortar. The sap is then applied to the middle leaves of the test plant by gentle rubbing either with the finger or a flattened glass spatula with a ground glass face. The thing to remember is that the rubbing should be gentle. It is necessary to cause a slight wound such as the breaking of the leaf hairs, because otherwise the virus cannot enter, but rough treatment will defeat its own ends. A virus must have a living

FIG. 4

Inoculating plants with viruses: dusting the leaves lightly with carborundum powder

cell in which to multiply, so that any treatment which kills the
cells prevents the fulfilment of the first necessity of a virus.

When two or three leaves of the test plant have been rubbed
with the virus-containing sap, they should be washed over, either
with a wash bottle (Fig. 7, p. 136) or under the tap, to remove
any excess inoculum. As a rule, it is advisable to grind up the
leaves in the mortar together with a fine abrasive such as grade F
carborundum powder. This makes numerous minute wounds in
the leaf epidermis and the number of entry points for the virus
is thereby greatly increased. The inoculated plants are then set
aside to await the development of symptoms. Finally, the hands
should be thoroughly washed with soap and warm water, and

FIG. 5
Inoculating plants with viruses: grinding up the infected leaf in a
mortar to obtain the inoculum

the pestle and mortar boiled for at least ten minutes. These precautions are necessary to prevent unwanted contamination of other plants. Figs. 4-7 illustrate the methods of inoculating plants with viruses.

USEFUL INDICATORS OR TEST PLANTS FOR COMMON VIRUS DISEASES

Before enumerating the various plants which can be used to indicate the presence of a virus in another plant, it will be well to consider what viruses we are most likely to find in farm or garden crops. If we are testing ornamental plants, the two most likely viruses will be those of *tomato spotted wilt* and *cucumber mosaic*. Chrysanthemums are frequently infected with a virus which causes distortions of the flowers. In tomato and tobacco

FIG. 6

Inoculating plants with viruses: rubbing the virus-containing sap
lightly over the leaves

plants the common viruses will be *tomato mosaic* and the closely
related *tobacco mosaic*, and possibly the two first-named viruses
and potato virus Y in tobacco as well. If potato plants are being
tested there are two common viruses which are almost certain
to be present; these are potato virus X, causing potato mild
mosaic and potato virus Y, causing leaf drop streak or severe
mosaic.

There are two other viruses commonly attacking cabbages
and cauliflowers which must be mentioned. These cause cabbage
black ringspot and cauliflower mosaic. The first-named of these
two is frequently found infecting wallflowers, especially the
Blood Red variety, in which it causes a yellow striping of the
petals (Frontispiece). This is an especially easy virus to test for.

These are the commonest viruses. which are also the most
frequently met with in farm and garden crops. They all have

FIG. 7
Inoculating plants with viruses: washing off the excess inoculum

one property in common, and that is that they are transmissible by inoculation of the sap. Not all plant viruses have this property, as we have already seen (Chap. 2).

Now as to the test plants for these viruses; the first and most important is the tobacco plant and the growing of this should present no difficulty, owing to the large amount of " backyard " tobacco-growing that is now going on. The seed can be easily obtained from any reputable seedsman or from one of the tobacco growers' associations. The Virginia or Burley types are the most suitable. The seed, which is very small, should be sown sparingly in a seed-box with a good compost and pricked out into pots whilst the seedlings are still very small. A tobacco seedling is ready for inoculation when it has two or three lower leaves about two or three inches long. The tobacco plant is susceptible to a great many viruses and will react to the majority of the common viruses we have mentioned.

There are three main types of response to inoculation with viruses: (1) A " picking out " in yellow or " clearing " of the veins of the youngest leaves. This symptom usually develops from seven to ten days after inoculation. It is followed some days later by (2) a general mottling of the other leaves, producing what is called a " mosaic " disease. Several of the viruses we have mentioned behave in this way. They are those of tobacco mosaic, potato virus Y, chrysanthemum mosaic and to a less extent cucumber mosaic. (3) Local lesions; these are spots of dead tissue which develop only on the leaf inoculated and usually appear from three to five days after inoculation, depending on the light and temperature prevailing at the time.

Let us now examine in more detail the reaction of our first test plant, the tobacco, to the common viruses we have mentioned. Actually, it is susceptible to all these viruses with the exception of cauliflower mosaic virus. With tomato spotted wilt, the first sign of infection is the development of a few rather large local lesions which may spread through the leaf and cause its death. The other signs of infection with this virus may take the form of concentric rings on the leaves; but in tobacco the more usual signs are large patches of dead cells followed by a general wilting. With cucumber mosaic virus there are few signs of primary infection; there may be slight clearing of the veins but this is easily missed. So a faint mottling and some malformation of the leaves are probably all that the beginner will recognise for this virus on tobacco.

The usual strains of tomato mosaic which, as we have already stated, is a strain of the tobacco mosaic virus, give only local lesions on the inoculated leaves of the tobacco plant without any subsequent mottling of the older leaves. These lesions may be quite numerous, are small and dark reddish in colour, and do not spread.

The ordinary or type strain of tobacco mosaic virus differs from the above in giving no local lesions, but a fairly bright " clearing of the veins " develops on the young leaves a week or ten days after inoculation. This is followed by a bold mottling or mosaic of the whole plant. Frequently, the leaves are distorted and may show large green islands or blisters of tissue on the normal green background of the leaf. This virus is extremely infectious and only a touch by a contaminated hand or implement is sufficient to pass on the disease.

Incidentally, to digress for a moment, an interesting experiment is to obtain infection in tobacco plants by virus out of cigarettes or pipe tobacco. Most commercial brands of cigarettes contain tobacco mosaic virus in an infectious condition, and infection of tobacco plants can usually be brought about. A few cigarettes should be pounded up with a little water and the resulting paste can be wiped gently with the finger over the leaves of the tobacco plants. By this method some unusual strains of the virus causing extreme distortion of the leaves can sometimes be obtained.

The next virus on our list is one from chrysanthemums which causes malformation of the flowers. This virus also infects tobacco and produces a disease superficially very similar to tobacco mosaic; it is doubtful indeed whether the novice would recognise any difference between them. However, a little further investigation will soon show the difference, and for this we need another test plant, *Nicotiana glutinosa*. If the virus causing the mosaic in the tobacco plant is due to the tobacco mosaic virus, inoculation to *N. glutinosa* produces in quite a short time, 3-4 days, large numbers of local lesions on the inoculated leaves. The chrysanthemum virus produces no lesions but, instead, the infected plant develops very distorted leaves which may produce outgrowths or may have no lamina and look like " shoestrings."

Coming now to the two common potato viruses, X and Y, both these infect tobacco with great ease. It is with potato virus X that we come across a good case of a " latent virus." Many potato varieties which appear perfectly healthy and normal nevertheless are infected with this virus and inoculation with the potato sap to tobacco seedlings will soon reveal its presence. Recognition of potato virus X on tobacco is a little difficult at first because the virus exists in a number of different strains which vary in the effect produced on the tobacco plant. If the strain is a virulent one, local lesions in the form of rings will develop, and later such rings will appear all over the plant. On the other hand, a mild strain will produce a rather faint mottling of the leaves. Potato virus Y is more uniform in its behaviour, and the first sign of infection of the tobacco plant is a fairly pronounced " clearing of the veins " of the young leaves. This is followed by a characteristic dark green colour along the veins, known as " vein banding."

The last virus for which the tobacco plant can be used as a test is one of the two common viruses attacking cabbages, cauliflowers and other plants belonging to the same family. As already mentioned, this virus frequently attacks the blood-red wallflower, causing the colour to " break " in the form of yellow streaks or stripes. If one or two petals showing this colour change are ground up in the mortar with a few drops of water and the resulting fluid rubbed gently on to the leaves of tobacco, the plant will respond in a characteristic manner. From five to ten days after the inoculation, according to the conditions, a small number of local lesions develop on the rubbed leaves. These lesions are small at first but grow slightly and have a whitish centre with a red periphery. No further spread of the virus takes place. If, however, the petal sap is inoculated into the other species of *Nicotiana* (*N. glutinosa*), a mosaic disease which permeates the whole plant results. This is a good example of how differently plants react to the same virus, and it is worth noting that this is the exact opposite of the behaviour of the tobacco mosaic virus on the same two plant species. It may be recollected that the type strain of the tobacco mosaic virus gave a mosaic mottle in tobacco and local lesions without further spread in *N. glutinosa*. But the virus from wallflowers (cabbage black ringspot virus it is called), as we have just seen, behaves in a reverse manner.

Another common virus which is easy to test for is known as tobacco necrosis virus. It was given this name because it was originally found in the roots of tobacco plants, but from our present point of view it is chiefly important as causing a severe and stunting disease of tulips; it is especially common in bulbs from Holland. To test for the presence of this virus, the french bean plant should be used. When the first pair of leaves is fully developed, they should be inoculated in the manner described with sap from the leaves of a suspected tulip. After about five or six days, if the virus is present, numerous reddish spots will develop on the inoculated leaves. These spots, or lesions, increase somewhat in size and may spread right through the leaf. As a rule, however, there is no further spread of the virus out of the leaf into the rest of the plant.

TRANSMITTING VIRUSES BY MEANS OF INSECTS

In Chapter 3 we have described some of the interesting relationships between insects and viruses, and the reader may like to try some simple experiments on these lines for himself. Some of the viruses we have already mentioned in the section on inoculation are easily transmitted by insects, and also one other which in nature is only transmitted in this manner and cannot be spread by sap-inoculation. In the British Isles the main insect vectors of plant viruses are several species of aphids, and the technique of handling them is a simple enough matter. All that is required is a small paint brush, a few lamp chimneys of the stable lantern type and some fine muslin. First of all, to procure the right kind of aphids, there are two species which will be best to use. One is known as the potato and peach aphid, or *Myzus persicae*, to give it its scientific name. The other aphid most easily recognisable and procurable is the black bean aphid, which is common enough in gardens on broad beans. The scientific name of this is *Aphis fabae*.

The potato and peach aphid is very widespread, and in the spring it can usually be found in large colonies on peach trees, on which trees it passes the winter in the egg stage. Later in the season, it is common on potatoes and brassica crops. It is a small green aphid (but on occasion may be reddish brown) and can be recognised by a slight dilatation of the cornicles or siphons on either side of the tail. This insect will transmit several of the viruses we mentioned; a good one to start with would be that of cucumber mosaic. We must assume that a cucumber or marrow plant infected with cucumber mosaic is available or, failing these, a tobacco plant which has been experimentally infected with the virus. In order to get the best results, it will be well to starve the aphids for an hour or so by putting them in a dry tube or small tin box. They should then be placed gently on the infected cucumber or tobacco plant, using the small paint brush, slightly moistened, to lift up the insects. Allow them to feed for about twenty to thirty minutes and then remove them to small tobacco plants, three or four aphids per plant. Before removing feeding aphids from a plant, it is well to touch them gently with the brush to make them withdraw their mouth-parts from the plant tissue, otherwise the fine stylets are liable to be broken off. Once the aphids have been placed on the experimental tobacco plants, they can be left to feed overnight and removed in the morning.

Fig. 8

How to confine virus-carrying aphids to the experimental plant

A convenient method of confining the aphids to the experimental plants is to place over the plant a glass chimney of the stable or hurricane lantern type. A circle of fine muslin is placed round the neck of the glass and held in place by means of a rubber ring, whilst the base is pressed into the soil surrounding the plant (Fig. 8). If the experiment has been successful, the young tobacco plants will begin to show symptoms of disease in a week or ten days.

A similar experiment can be carried out with sugar-beet mosaic, and either of the two species of aphids mentioned can be used for this. Examination of practically any field of sugar-beet, or row of spinach beet, will reveal plants with a light and dark green mottling of the leaves. There is no need to dig up the plant; a couple of the younger leaves will suffice. The aphids should be treated as before, and allowed to feed on the diseased leaves, but this time it is necessary to use young beet or mangold seedlings as test-plants, since the virus will not infect tobacco plants.

All the viruses we have dealt with so far in this chapter have been those which can be transmitted from plant to plant by mechanical inoculation of the sap. We come now to a common virus of the potato which cannot be spread in this manner, but depends upon the aphid for its transmission. The disease it causes is known as potato leaf-roll because of the characteristic upward rolling of the leaves. Examples of the disease can usually be found in most potato crops. Unlike the experiments with cucumber mosaic and sugar-beet mosaic, the aphids must be allowed to feed on the potato leaf-roll plant for a much longer period, and they should be left on the plant for twenty-four hours at least. Since the tobacco plant is not susceptible to the leaf-roll virus, we must use some other test plant, and in this case seedlings of *Physalis angulata* serve the purpose admirably. Symptoms develop in about ten days after the transfer of the aphids and the infected plants are easily recognised from their yellow colour, dwarfing and rolled leaves.

GRAFTING

Another method of conveying virus from one plant to another is by means of grafting. There are various ways of doing this, but the simplest is the *cleft graft*. The easiest plants to graft are the potato, tomato and tobacco, and each one of these can be grafted on the other.

To make a cleft graft, cut off a growing point with a few inches of stem and remove all the leaves except the youngest. Then with a sharp knife or razor blade cut the stem to a V-shape (Fig. 9a), but be careful not to cut through the stem. This is called the scion and as a rule it is taken from the virus-infected

plant. Next, select a healthy plant, called
the " stock," cut through a stem which
is sappy and not too woody; it is better
if the cut passes through a node, otherwise the stem may be hollow and
difficult to graft. Now cut vertically and
centrally through the stem for a distance
a little greater than the length of the V-
shaped stem of the scion (Fig. 9b). Insert
the scion in the slit in the stem and,
holding it in position, bind the two
together with a piece of bast previously
boiled to soften it, taking care that the
bast lies smoothly against the stem and
does not become twisted. A better
material to use than bast, if it can be

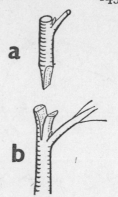

Fig. 9
Method of cleft-grafting
for non-woody plants:
A, scion; B, stock

obtained, is thin rubber tape about one-quarter inch wide, such
as is found in the middle of golf balls. This can be wound round
the graft and holds itself in position by its elasticity. The loose
end of the tape is secured by means of a drop of ordinary rubber
solution.

When the graft is finished, the plant should be placed in a
moist atmosphere away from direct sunlight for a few days to
allow organic union to take place; under the bench in the
glasshouse will probably serve the purpose. The graft union
should be complete in ten days or so.

In doing grafts of this kind it is of importance to note that
only closely related plants may be grafted to each other. Thus
it is useless trying to graft, say, cucumbers to tobacco plants,
though the former graft quite readily to marrow and white bryony
(*Bryonia dioica*). Similarly tobacco, tomato and potato plants
may be grafted together and to related plants such as henbane
and the various nightshades.

A simple and almost invariably successful method of grafting
is by *inarching*, and this can be applied to plants with long,
flexible stems, for example tomato or cucumber plants. In this
method of grafting, a notch is cut in the stems of each plant, in

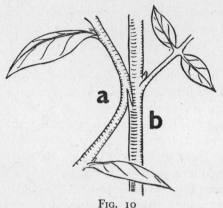

FIG. 10
Inarch method of grafting

the one slanting upwards and in the other downwards. The flaps so made are then fitted into each other and bound together, and the union takes place as before (Fig. 10). When this has happened, the appropriate stems may be cut, leaving either plant on the roots of the other.

Other forms of grafting can be experimented with, tuber grafting, for example, and the use of the parasitic plant, dodder (*Cuscuta* spp).

In grafting potato tubers, the only apparatus needed is a set of cork borers, which may be obtained from any laboratory supplier. Select two borers of suitable diameter, one a size larger than the other; with the smaller of the two cut out a core from the tuber to be grafted, being careful to include an eye. Then with the larger borer cut out a core with eye from the tuber suspected of virus infection and push this core into the hole made in the healthy tuber. By reason of its slightly larger size, the core will fit tightly in place. The tuber can then be planted as usual, and the first core taken out to make room for the graft should also be planted as a " control." That is, it should be grown into a plant to compare with the plant produced by the grafted tuber. This will show whether the grafted tuber was really healthy in the first instance. A slightly more difficult experiment is to graft tulip bulbs. This can be done by inserting a plug in a somewhat similar manner to that described, or by cutting two bulbs in half, just avoiding the growing point, and then binding the two halves firmly together. The virus which is best transmitted by this method is that causing the change in flower colour known as tulip break, so that it is important to choose a bulb from a plant known to be infected with this virus and one from a known healthy tulip.

It is necessary to take a few more precautions in dealing with tulip bulbs than with potato tubers because of the risk of secondary fungal infections. The cork borer should be heated or boiled, and the point of insertion of the plug should be covered over with a little melted paraffin wax. Similarly, the halves of the two bulbs should be bound together with bast which has been boiled and the join sealed with wax as above.

The parasitic plant, dodder, can be used as a means of grafting, simply by allowing it to parasitise a virus-infected plant and then to grow on from that to another plant which is healthy. This method has been used by virus workers to transfer viruses from unsuitable hosts to plants more suitable for study. The dodder plant, however, is somewhat selective in its action and does not transmit every virus.

In this short account of some of the simpler methods of plant virus study, only the most commonly occurring viruses have been dealt with. With increasing experience other viruses will be found and tests can be made of a wider range of garden crops.

Glossary and
Table : Testing for Common
Plant Viruses

GLOSSARY

Antibiotic: A substance produced by fungi and other organisms which has the power of destroying bacteria.

Antibody: A specific substance, protein in nature, which is produced by animals when certain substances (antigens) are injected into their bloodstream. Antibodies have the power of combining with, and neutralising, antigens.

Antigen: A substance which induces the formation of antibodies when injected into the bloodstream of an animal, in plant viruses usually a rabbit.

Aucuba mosaic: So named from the resemblance of the virus disease to the normal appearance of the variegated Japanese laurel *Aucuba japonica variegata*.

Bacteriophages: Literally " Bacterium eaters "; now known as bacterial viruses.

Berkefeld Filter: A filter made of diatomaceous earth for removing bacteria from a solution.

Break: Change in the colour of a flower due to infection with a virus.

Brownian Movement: Irregular movement of small particles in solution due to their bombardment by the molecules of the surrounding medium (also applied to the movement of atoms and molecules in liquids and gases due to their thermal energy).

Capsular Disease: A virus disease of insects in which the blood is filled with minute capsules each containing a rod-shaped virus particle. (See polyhedral bodies.)

Carcinogen: A substance which has the power, when applied to tissues, of initiating the production of malignant tumours.

Complex: When two or more viruses are present together in an organism, causing a distinct disease, this is known as a complex.

Dark-field Illumination: Method of examining an object under the optical microscope whereby the object is seen brightly illuminated against a dark background.

Dodecahedra (rhombic): Crystals bounded by twelve faces, all of which are diamond-shaped.

Enations: Leaf-like outgrowths on the undersides of leaves (generally caused by virus infection).

Epidermis: The outer tissue layer of animals and plants.

Filter Plant: A plant which, by reason of its immunity to one of two viruses in a disease complex, can be used to separate the viruses by filtering out one of them when inoculated with the complex.

Hemiptera: Group of sap-sucking insects.

Heterogenesis: Arising *de novo*, or spontaneous generation.

Indicator Plant: One which reacts to infection with a given virus in a rapid and characteristic fashion.

Inoculation: The procedure of introducing virus-containing material into a living organism by any means (injection, grafting, etc.).

Intramuscular: Into a muscle.

Keratinized: Horny.

Labium: In Hemiptera, the rostrum or beak which supports the stylets sliding within it.

Leukaemia: A blood disease similar in nature to cancer, in which the number of white cells increases and the number of red cells decreases.

Lysogenic bacteria: Bacteria containing a latent virus which will lyse or destroy other susceptible bacteria.

Malignant: In tumours, malignancy is characterised by the inability of the organism to prevent the growth spreading through the tissues and into the circulation and thus to other organs where it establishes itself anew.

Metamorphosis: A dramatic change occurring during development (especially the series of changes through which an insect passes in its growth from egg through larva and pupa to adult).

Metastase: The breaking away of cells from a tumour to form a fresh tumour in another place.

Millimicron: A millionth of a millimetre: one twenty-five millionth of an inch, written mμ.

Mosaic: Name given to a plant virus disease which causes mottling of the leaves.

Necrosis: Death of the cells of an organism.

Neoplastic: Pertaining to new growth of a tissue, or tissues, not subject to the normal control mechanism of the organism (see malignant).

Nucleus: A body found in most cells and considered to be the part carrying the hereditary characters of the organism and controlling the cells' growth and activity.

Nymph: Young form of an insect without a metamorphosis.

Paracrystal: A body having a regular arrangement of its constituent molecules in two dimensions in space. A crystal is arranged regularly in all three dimensions, i.e. in length, breadth and thickness.

Pathogenic: Disease causing.

Pharyngeal: Belonging to the pharynx.

Phloem: Part of the vascular tissue of plants, acting as a store and transporter of nutrients.

Plasmagene: A postulated self-propagating particle, transmitted by heredity, but lying outside the nucleus.

Polyhedral bodies: Many-sided crystals which occur in the blood and tissues of caterpillars infected with a certain type of virus disease.

Protein: The basic substances from which living matter is built. They contain nitrogen, hydrogen, carbon and oxygen and small amounts of sulphur.

Rhombic: See dodecahedra.

Rickettsia: Obligate pathogenic organisms intermediate in size and character between the larger animal viruses and the smallest bacteria.

Sarcoma: A tumour of connective tissue.

Scion: In grafting of plants, that part which is devoid of its own root.

Serial passage: Progressive inoculation of a virus or other pathogen through a series of susceptible hosts.

Serological: Used to describe tests made with antiserum. (See Antibody and Antigen.)

Stylets: The piercing mouth structures which occur in the insect orders Hemiptera and Diptera.

Systemic: Generally distributed throughout the plant.

Tumour: An abnormal growth of a tissue.

Vaccination: Originally protection from smallpox by causing a mild disease with vaccinia virus, now generally applied to any immunisation by injecting killed or attenuated organisms.

Vascular bundle: Tissue in plants composed among other things of xylem and phloem (q.v.) and serving both for food and water transport and for mechanical strengthening.

Vector: An insect, or other arthropod, or any other organism which transmits a virus.

Vegetative propagation: Propagation by means other than the true seed (grafting, tubers, rhizomes, etc.).

Viruliferous: Virus carrying.

Xylem: The woody tissue of plants.

TABLE

Infected Crop	Test Plant	Symptoms	Virus
Tomato with leaf mottling	*Nicotiana glutinosa*	Local spots on inoculated leaves	Tomato mosaic
Tomato with bronzing of leaves	Tobacco	Large local spots with tendency to spread, followed by wilting	Tomato spotted wilt
Tomato with fernlike leaves	Tobacco	Slight mottling of leaves	Cucumber mosaic
Potato, slight mosaic mottling on leaves	Tobacco	Usually local spots, sometimes in the form of rings, on the inoculated leaves, followed by mottling	Potato Virus X
Potato, leaves dead and hanging down, streaks on stem	Tobacco	Clearing of the veins of the youngest leaves, followed by a dark-green banding of the veins	Potato Virus Y
Dahlia, mottling of leaves and stunting of plant	Tobacco	Slight mottling of leaves	Cucumber mosaic
Dahlia, mottling of leaves with tendency to ring formation	Tobacco	Large local spots with tendency to spread, followed by wilting	Tomato spotted wilt
Tulip, much distortion and deformation	French bean	Local reddish spots on inoculated leaves	Tobacco necrosis

Iufected Crop	Test Plant	Symptoms	Virus
Chrysanthemum, flowers much distorted	Tobacco	A bold dark and light-green mottling	Chrysanthemum flower-distorting virus
Wallflowers, streaking or striping of the petals, some mottling of the leaves (similar symptoms on Stocks)	Tobacco	Local spots on inoculated leaves, light centre with reddish rim	Cabbage black ringspot virus
Broccoli, distortion of plant, failure to heart; crinkling and curling of leaves	Tobacco	Local spots on inoculated leaves, light centre with reddish rim	Cabbage black ringspot virus
Broccoli, some distortion of plant, leaves show a dark-green banding of the veins	Cauliflower seedlings	Clearing of the veins, followed by mottling	Cauliflower mosaic virus

Index

INDEX

THE NEW NATURALIST LIBRARY

" What must impress the readers of the volumes is that they are at once books for the expert and the general reader, a combination not easy to achieve." GLASGOW HERALD

FLEAS, FLUKES & CUCKOOS
MIRIAM ROTHSCHILD AND THERESA CLAY

" A popular classic about one of the most fascinating branches of biology: Parasitism. Written with the clarity and passion that distinguishes great natural history." LILLIPUT

Many other books are in active preparation. If you wish to be kept informed of each one as it appears please write to Collins, 14 St James's Place, London, S.W. 1., giving your name and address.

THE HERRING GULL'S WORLD
NIKO TINBERGEN

" It takes a very long period of watching to become really familiar with an animal and to attain a deeper understanding of its behaviour; and without the love for the animal itself, no observer, however patient, could ever look at it long enough to make valuable observations on its behaviour. If Karl von Frisch's name will, for all future time, be associated with the honey-bee, Niko Tinbergen's will always call to mind his work on gulls. He has been observing and analysing the behaviour of the gull family for decades. This is not just a book on gulls: it is a book on those animals whose behaviour has been more thoroughly analysed than any others. And it is the work of an expert, who writes with charm, clarity and precision."   KONRAD LORENZ

THE FULMAR
JAMES FISHER

" No species of British bird has ever been monographed so completely as the Fulmar is in this splendid volume, and none can be a more worthy subject for so exhaustive a study. The author's researches have given us a book that is an example of scientific field ornithology at its best. He is to be congratulated in successfully accomplishing this monumental work, which will be a standard for many years to come."   ZOO LIFE

" His book will be relied upon by specialists and will be prized by bird-watchers and lovers of the islands and wild places whose atmosphere and charm he has so well re-created out of his passion for the subject."
                                        MAX NICHOLSON *in the* OBSERVER

THE BADGER
ERNEST NEAL

" Mr. Neal's book has thrilled me as few books have done in the past twenty years or so; it has held my attention for every line of every page."
                                BRIAN VESEY-FITZGERALD *in the* FIELD

" He has accumulated a mass of information from direct observation, he has discovered new facts and solved mysteries of long standing, and he has written his book in such a way that every interested person can read it with ease and profit. The book is illustrated with the finest collection of badger photographs I have yet seen and their number and variety is far beyond anything that has been done before. You can't be interested in the badger and be without this unique book."   SCOTTISH FIELD

FLOWERS OF THE COAST
IAN HEPBURN

" It is a description of the wild flowers of the various types of habitat found around the coast of Britain, and is written in a simple straightforward manner which will be understood and enjoyed by all who read it. Though this is a book for the layman, there is much for the expert to enjoy. It is a book to take on a seaside holiday, and will stimulate the interest in well-known places, and inspire budding ecologists to seek new ground." WATSONIA

" This is primarily a work for the student of flowers, written by a botanist of the highest repute. But it has also a strong appeal for all who visit the varying coasts of our islands and wonder at the richness of their vegetation." DAILY MAIL

BRITISH PLANT LIFE
W. B. TURRILL

" A fascinating and highly successful attempt to explain to the intelligent reader some of the factors that have determined the range and form of British plants, and the means by which we can learn more of these factors. Schools and colleges will find this book indispensable. It is indeed a triumph that one volume should in text and illustrations unite so much beauty with the strict discipline of science." WESTERN MAIL

" We strongly recommend it to all academic students of botany and to the many more amateur specialists who are making flowering plant life their special line." L. J. F. BRIMBLE *in* NATURE

WILD ORCHIDS OF BRITAIN
V. S. SUMMERHAYES

" Almost everything that anyone can want to know about the British orchids is here. An excellent key is provided. This is a book that demands several readings. It is destined to be the standard work on the subject. But it is much more interesting and much more vital than those awful words ' standard work ' would lead anyone to suppose. I, at least, was fascinated."
BRIAN VESEY-FITZGERALD *in* OUT OF DOORS

" A botanical work of outstanding importance. It will appeal to all wild-flower-loving countrymen." COUNTRYMAN

" Really the first serious monograph on the native orchids to be published at a reasonable price. It should be (and without any doubt will be) in the hands of all British orchidomaniacs. . . . Mr. Summerhayes has written an extremely scholarly and comprehensive monograph."
JOCELYN BROOKE *in* TIME AND TIDE